INTERPRETING THE WEATHER

**A Practical Guide for Householders,
Gardeners, Motorists and Sportsmen**

INTERPRETING THE
WEATHER

INGRID HOLFORD

DAVID & CHARLES : NEWTON ABBOT

To all the friends who have asked me
what I can possibly find to write about
the weather

0 7153 5800 6

Set in 12/13 Bembo
by C. E. Dawkins (Typesetters) Ltd
London SE1
and printed in Great Britain
by Pitman Press Bath
for David & Charles (Holdings) Limited
South Devon House Newton Abbot Devon

CONTENTS

LIST OF ILLUSTRATIONS

All photographs are by the author except where otherwise stated

CHAPTER ONE

PARTNERS IN WEATHER FORECASTING

THE AMATEUR

In view of the eccentricities of most climates it is odd that the idea of 'talking about the weather' is almost synonymous with having nothing worth while to say. It is certainly not because the subject does not concern us—we often desire desperately to know how the weather will progress—but perhaps because of a suspicion that the whole subject is too erudite for the average layman. The **very** name of the science, meteorology, is tongue twisting, and the textbooks are so peppered with technicalities that it is easy to despair before even starting to understand. At the same time the almost reverential awe with which the forecasting abilities of farmers and sailors are discussed indicate how much we would like to have the same ability ourselves.

The admiration is justified. When livelihoods depend upon the weather, men watch like hawks for the signs that tell them what will happen next. Constant observation of sky and horizon leads imperceptibly and without effort to predicting how these will change in the near future. When the breadwinner is a shrewd weather observer, his children unconsciously acquire the habit too, probably gaining in turn the reputation for being 'better than the

Met Office'. Traditional learning like this is a slow business, but there is no magic to it. The long years of observation can in fact be by-passed with a little concentration on a few scientific principles which we expect our junior schoolchildren to be able to learn. By watching the sky, by working out what has caused the particular misery of the day, fog, cloud or rain, and by noting developments hour by hour, it is quite possible soon to answer one's own short-range queries about the weather. Is it a day to take a raincoat, or a day to hoe the garden, or a day to go to the seaside?

Competent observation need take little time. A sniff of fresh air at the window in the morning, a frequent glance at the sky from indoors or out, a little contemplation while waiting in the bus queue, and the weather picture can be yours. What you can't see with your eyes, you can observe with ears or nose; the clearer noise of distant trains or the pungent smell from a local factory should tell you automatically of change in wind direction. Nothing is too small to be noted.

THE PROFESSIONAL METEOROLOGIST

There is however a definite limit to what one can do oneself. Weather is a worldwide phenomenon and it is not possible to forecast for many hours ahead without knowing what is happening outside the area of our vision.

Professional meteorologists have access to a worldwide weather information network from which reports pour in continually, day and night, by teleprinter, radio, wireless, radar and satellite photography. This information is plotted on to maps and graphs, and provides the basis for official forecasts. But much as technology has advanced, it is still not possible to get instantaneous coverage on weather conditions everywhere and issue a forecast a minute later. The whole picture builds up gradually: surface weather of a country within half an hour of the observations being made; upper air data next; not till several hours later all the foreign information necessary for worldwide analysis. The plotted maps and graphs then have to be analysed carefully before a forecast is made for transmission to the public.

The frustrating thing is that no sooner is one complete weather picture on paper than it is already out of date. Moreover, forecasting is rarely a case of simple projection of the existing pattern a few paces onward. Weather travels, but it alters at the same time. Not only do the rise and fall of existing systems have to be forecast, but the genesis of completely new ones. Meteorology, like medicine, comes into the category of inexact sciences. Here there are no mathematical certainties, and it is useless to expect any; there are only probabilities, various degrees of likelihood.

The problem of communicating the maximum information in a minimum of space is tackled by the meteorologist, as by the geographer, by means of maps. One picture conveys more in a moment than a whole stream of descriptive words, and since weather charts are drawn according to an international code they can be understood anywhere in the world. They are not difficult to interpret, and one glance at an official chart each day is better than any amount of time spent on so-called 'popular' maps that merely divide an area into sections and put words across them— or umbrellas or fur coats or bikinis! These simply show the forecaster's *present* opinion, without showing the evidence on which it is based, and they allow the layman no scope for amending a forecast in the light of local observations as the day progresses. It is as inevitable that some forecasts go awry as that some medical diagnoses go wrong. Intelligent interpretation by the layman of local warning symptoms can minimise the trouble caused. I hope that this book will show him how to do so.

MODERN TECHNOLOGY

Sometimes the enthusiasm with which one tries to acquire weather knowledge is tempered by a belief that before long some super-machine will take over the job for us. It is as well not to let the imagination dwell on eventualities which may never be realised.

In the middle of the nineteenth century scientists were convinced that the only way to tackle the problem of forecasting was by using 'pure laboratory' methods. They believed that, given the basic facts of temperature, pressure and humidity, it should be possible to forecast by formula. There were two main snags to this idealistic approach. The laboratory in which weather is manufactured is the whole world and there were then few technical facilities for collecting and assimilating data on this scale. And they hadn't yet got any sophisticated formulae. So the belief didn't get them very far and they had to accept what they thought of as second-best, the empirical approach used by Admiral Fitzroy when he was Chief Meteorologist to the Board of Trade between 1854 and 1865. This method was to note prevailing conditions and to forecast by advancing the conditions according to their known speeds or behaviour. The invention of the telegraph made possible the collection of simultaneous surface weather observations from strategically positioned stations, and a plotting system evolved, similar to that in use today. Constant study of repetitive weather sequences enabled satisfactory prediction rules to be deduced, culminating in this century with the theories of air masses and depressions which will be outlined in this book.

Meanwhile, the advance of technology brought sophisticated self-reporting instruments which could be sent aloft by balloon to add upper air data to that collected at ground level, and teleprinters facilitated the relay of weather observations. The urgent necessity for accurate weather information during the second world war gave a further impetus to meteorological method. Aircraft carried weather instruments and made regular flights for the specific purpose of collecting data, mainly over the Atlantic whence most of British weather comes.

Today better self-reporting instruments are flown still higher into the atmosphere or left unattended at remote corners of the earth; radar is used to help detect clouds capable of producing rain; satellites ceaselessly encompass the world and send back a

Photograph taken from satellite Nimbus 3, 29 March 1970, coastline superimposed—the cloud pattern confirms the classical textbook situation of a low-pressure wind circulation with associated warm and cold fronts

stream of photographs which miraculously confirm that textbook theories really do happen (see above); facsimile transmitting machines eliminate much multiplication of effort by enabling charts drawn at a central office to be sent direct to outstations. Most important of all, the computer has appeared to digest and deal with more information in half an hour than a human brain can manage in a lifetime. The information gleaned by these methods all over the world is pooled and re-distributed according to agreed specifications and time schedules by an international organisation whose amicable workings must be the envy of politicians.

Meanwhile, mathematicians have helped the physicists to shape their meteorological theories into formidable formulae. Awesome programmes are fed into computers and answers are drawn automatically on to charts to give predicted pressure patterns for twenty-four hours ahead. These were treated with extreme caution at first by forecasters who preferred to use their own 'hand-made' ones. The two kinds of chart were continually checked against each other, and eventually those made by machine proved so reliable that they have now virtually taken over this particular task.

The digestive capacities of computers will probably increase and there is little reason, bar cost, why the collection of data should not expand to meet this appetite. Nevertheless, it hardly seems possible that we can ever know every factor pertinent to the weather, everywhere on earth or in the atmosphere, at every moment of time. And any one factor missed may be just the one to set off a completely unexpected chain reaction in the weather. The longer the time lapse since the making of a forecast, the greater the error due to that first missed observation.

Hence long-range forecasts, based on computer material and deductions from similar sequences in the past, can only give broad trends and may never be able to specify weather for particular dates. They have proved their worth for farming projects, building programmes and similar long-term ventures, and can be expected to improve up to a certain limit. But they are never likely to be able to pinpoint, for instance, the most suitable day and time for next month's garden fête.

With short-range forecasts, there is plenty of scope for improving the conveyance of weather information to the public.

Dial-a-forecast and dial-a-weather-map (or satellite picture) are services within our reach already if we have the inclination and money to demand them. The accuracy of such forecasts will probably improve too, but they are likely always to remain of a general nature. Weather is so profoundly influenced by local contours, proximity to sea, protection from wind and so on, that no instruments are ever likely to be able to tailor a forecast for an individual enquirer. The detail we must fill in ourselves and by learning to do so we make a big step forward towards a satisfactory forecasting system. I, for one, find it encouraging to think that in an increasingly technological age there is still room for human skill in forecasting.

CHAPTER TWO

TRANSFERENCE OF HEAT

A basic necessity for plant, animal and human life as we know it is the light and heat of the sun. In moderation, of course. Our world is a cautious 93 million miles away from the sun. The ceaseless rotation of the earth on its axis ensures that any one area receives sunshine for only a limited period each day. Because the axis is tilted to the plane in which the earth rotates round the sun every year, the relative height from which we receive sunshine varies according to the season. The more nearly overhead, the more the rays are concentrated on a smaller area and therefore the more heat is received. All of which ensures that no section of the earth has life scorched or frozen out of existence because of too much or too little heat.

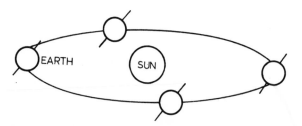

The tilted axis of the earth causes our seasons

The price we pay for this control system is weather. Because of temperature difference in various parts of the world, the surrounding airs react to produce wind, cloud and rain. Not only do the large-scale differences in temperature determine the broad outlines of weather, but local or even domestic variations can alter weather for any one person, animal or plant.

RADIATION AND CONDUCTION

If two objects have different temperatures, heat will flow from the one with the higher temperature to the one with the lower temperature.

The transfer of heat may be accomplished by direct absorption by the cooler object of heat rays emitted by the warmer one. To take an example from the kitchen, meat placed under a grill will cook by absorption of radiated heat from the grill.

Alternatively, the transfer of heat can be made by conduction, if the two objects are in contact. This is the case in frying. Heat is conducted from the source to the pan, and from the pan to its contents. Some substances are better conductors than others. Air is a poor conductor of heat and therefore acts as a good insulator, as, for example, between the outer and inner skins of cavity house walls, or between the human body and outside air by air spaces between fibres of clothing. Water, in contrast, is a good conductor of heat, hence its suitability for cooking. Whatever heat is conducted to the saucepan is then spread rapidly through the water or steam medium to cook the food contents evenly all over. If the saucepan boils dry, all the heat is then conducted to the bottom layer of food, which will soon burn.

In a weather context, heat radiated from the sun is distributed in several ways. A very little leaks by conduction direct to air en route to the earth and raises air temperature fractionally; some is reflected back or absorbed by clouds which intervene between us and the sun; and the remainder of the radiated heat reaches earth. A little of this is reflected back (light colours reflect more than dark, shiny surfaces more than rough) and the rest is absorbed by whatever it touches, raising temperature according to the substance of which the object is made. The difference is often considerable. In particular, to raise the temperature of a particle of water by $1°C$ requires something like five times the amount of heat needed to raise the temperature of an equal mass particle of rock by $1°C$. Moreover, since water is a good conductor, such heat spreads itself easily over a considerable depth of water. One day's sunshine will spread its benefit over a large volume of sea or river and, even in midsummer, will result in only a very small rise in temperature. It needs a whole summer of warmth before sea builds up to its maximum temperature in early autumn.

DISTRIBUTION OF HEAT IN SOIL

Dry soil consists of millions of particles of eroded rock. Not only does each particle rise quickly in temperature with quite a modest dose of sunshine, but each particle is insulated from others by air pockets. These make conduction of heat downwards into the soil a slow process and most of the heat received from the sun is devoted to raising the temperature of only a shallow layer of soil.

An open sandy soil has plenty of insulating air spaces, so most of the heat received remains near the surface and daily variations in surface temperature are very large. A closely compacted clay soil has fewer insulating air spaces and is therefore a much better conductor of heat. The heat it receives is spread more equably between surface and root level of plants and there is a smaller range of temperature variation at the surface.

The situation is complicated, however, by the fact that the insulating quality of the air spaces may be counteracted by the conducting quality of the water content in soil. Particles of soil are able to retain water in the spaces between them by surface tension and against the pull of gravity. Soil, therefore, fills from the top downwards. Not till all the top spaces hold as much water as they are able, and a further fall actually pushes the first lot downwards, will water penetrate. In an open soil the downward penetration will be fairly quick—think of the millions of children who try to fill their sand holes with buckets of sea water! In a closely compacted soil, penetration of water is very difficult and much may run to waste before soaking down. The golden rule for watering any garden soil should be 'lightly, but for long duration'.

At any one time, therefore, rain may cause soils of different consistency to have water to different depths. An open soil which is wet through may become as good a conductor of heat over a particular depth as a close soil which is only wet on the surface. Each particular situation must be gauged on the balance of relative factors and will vary between two extremes. Thoroughly wet closely compacted soil will be the best conductor and dry sand the worst. On a non-tidal beach in high sunshine, surface temperature can get hot enough to take the skin off bare feet, while an inch or so below the sand is quite cool.

As far as the weather is concerned, surface temperatures are what count. The important thing to remember is that within a matter of only a few yards between sea and shore, or between river and towpath or field, temperatures can be wildly different. The greatest differences are usually in early spring during a sunny day, when there may be high temperatures over land but still minimum seasonal temperature over water.

INSULATION

The reason why an approximate status quo is maintained in the heat-exchange account of the world is that everything on earth is also a radiating body to some extent, relinquishing heat where necessary to equalise temperature with its surroundings. Not only do man-made sources of heat like fires, electric irons and toasters radiate heat, but also human beings and animals with their ingenious system of converting food into heat, and inanimate things like walls and paths which have no means of self-replenishment. When the source of original heat is removed, be it electricity, food or sunshine, the objects thus heated continue to radiate heat outwards if free to do so and, if without replenishment, fall in temperature. Substances that readily rise in temperature also lose heat readily.

The only way to delay loss of heat by radiation is to insulate. Lag the boiler, clothe the human body, cover the garden plants. Similarly, a blanket of cloud will inhibit loss of heat from the earth, and because snow has the same sort of structure as soil, that is consisting of particles loosely packed with air spaces between, it too is a good insulator.

But note that no cover will itself *provide* heat; it merely helps to retain what there is. Hence lagging must be on the tank while it is still hot, cloches must be put back over plants well before sunset while there is still appreciable heat in the top soil, and cloud cover is needed early after dark if it is to prevent a steep drop in night-time temperatures. And the principle is vital for humans also. Faced with the prospect of having to spend a night in the open, lost in fog or hemmed in by snow, the time to take to sleeping bag or improvised burrow is while one is still warm and there is heat to conserve. In emergency treatment for hypothermia (dangerously low body temperature) the first essential is to prevent any *further* loss of body heat by wrapping closely in an airtight covering. Plastic sheeting will do. A hot bath may be part of the medical treatment for *replenishing* body heat, but lives have been saved merely by close contact with an animal or another human being.

Whether or not snow is beneficial in the garden depends upon whether it falls early in the season when there is still soil warmth to conserve, or whether it falls after a cold winter when soil is already frost-bound and damage done. On the roof of a greenhouse or piled against window frames it will exclude damaging draughts and help make the most of any meagre inside heating source. Otherwise it may merely add an extra damage factor, that of breakage from sheer weight of snow. It is advisable to shake heavy snow off bushes every now and then, but to leave it over glass if it is not too weighty.

The rate of snow clearance depends partly upon the conductivity of the surface upon which it is lying. Below is a photograph of my garden after a snowfall on unfrozen and moist soil. Heat from the subsoil has flowed upwards and assisted clearance from all the bare surface soil. The grass, low plants and unheated greenhouse roof are all still covered in snow; the air spaces beneath them have impeded any conduction of heat upwards from the soil.

CONVECTION

Direct reception of heat, either by interception of heat rays or by conduction, leaves one major feature of temperature change to be explained. How does *air* get heated? It is such a poor conductor that its temperature would lag much further behind soil or sea

Heat conducted upwards from the subsoil has helped clear snow over bare soil, but over grass, low plants and greenhouse roof, snow is insulated from the benefit of subsoil heat and persists

temperature than it does if there were not some other way of communicating heat. A mechanical principle comes into operation.

When a gas is heated, it becomes less dense. Consequently, if a shallow layer of air in contact with a hot surface warms by conduction it becomes lighter than the air above it. It acquires buoyancy, rises, and is replaced by a layer of heavier air from above, which in turn warms, rises and is replaced, and so on. Instead of warming by conduction from one layer to another, each layer descends in turn to take its place on the warming surface and after being warmed then moves upwards. This is why a cupboard with a hot-water tank at the top is not much use for airing clothes, whereas one with the tank at the bottom gives a warm dry air space above.

This process of heat transference is called convection, and it is put to good use indoors in modern systems of heating which replace the old-fashioned open coal fire. Radiant heat direct to the traditional semi-circle of people sitting around a coal fire gives glowing faces, chilly feet if there is even a shallow kerb, and cold backs which are themselves radiating heat into the colder regions

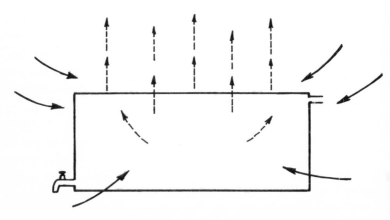

Air in contact with a hot radiator surface warms, becomes less dense, rises and is replaced by colder air which takes its turn on the warming surface

behind. The thin layers of air which warm successively on contact with the fire are smartly wafted upwards through the open chimney. In contrast, radiating surfaces warmed by electricity or hot water require no open outlet to the sky, and the successive layers of warmed air gradually fill the whole room. Fan heaters speed air movement and are able to heat large volumes of air with smaller but hotter radiating surfaces.

If air is in contact with a cooling body, the reverse happens. As the first layer cools on contact with the surface, it becomes more dense and loses buoyancy. If on a level surface, the cold air remains where it is, continuing to cool, and only very slowly transferring the cooling to the warmer layers of air above by conduction. If the cooling surface is a slope, then the cold air obeys the laws of gravity and slides downwards, the warmer air from above being drawn in to fill the gap and getting cooled in turn. This is why deep-freeze cabinets with top lids can be left open with impunity—the heavy air is in a state of stability, retained by the side walls. A front-opening freezer loses a lot of cold air every time the door is opened; like water from a dam, it flows out and downwards and is replaced by warmer air from the room.

The behaviour of air and water is in many ways similar because they are both fluids and are free to move about. Radiation cooling over a water surface is rather like a looking-glass reflection of the convective behaviour of air over heating land. The cooling top layer of water becomes denser, sinks, and is replaced by a warmer lighter layer from below, which in its turn cools and sinks. In this way cooling at night is spread over a large volume of water and has only very slight effect upon surface temperature in any one night. It needs a whole winter of cooling before sea temperature falls to its minimum. On a sunny day the sea is usually cooler than the land; on a clear night it will often be warmer.

The principles of radiation, conduction, buoyancy and non-buoyancy familiar to us all in our domestic life are exactly those used by nature in the production of weather.

CHAPTER THREE

WIND, THE MOVEMENT OF AIR

Movement of air caused by temperature differences is wind. The smallest winds we call draughts. In winter, carefully warmed air in our houses must rise and, unless we prevent it, the most eager replacement air is the coldest, which is outside. Knifelike draughts pour through badly fitting windows or gaps beneath doors at quite appreciable speeds.

SEA BREEZES AND LAND BREEZES

Out of doors, temperature differences occur wherever there are differences in surface substances. A tarred car park will heat more rapidly than an adjacent field, and air from the field will drift in to replace air rising over the car park. Air over a heated towpath rises and is replaced by cooler air from the adjacent river, while air higher over the river sinks to replace that drawn towards the towpath; a small circulation is formed which on a still summer's day the unobservant will deny exists, but which constantly proves itself by the fact that skilful yachtsmen can keep their sailing boats moving by these zephyrs alone.

One step upwards in scale, along the coast large areas of land heat rapidly in sunshine, air rises and a breeze is drawn in from the colder surface of the sea. Air above the sea sinks and is again pulled in over the land. This is a larger circulation than that taking place along the towpath, and it builds up during the day to a strength which varies according to the temperature difference causing it. A very hot summer sun may cause a sea breeze of about 15mph along the coast, felt in decreasing strength 15-20 miles inland. With good reason do holidaymakers leave the stifling heat of inland towns to trek to the coast. Even in spring and autumn enough breeze may blow by middle morning in a narrow coastal strip to make sea sailing possible because of local temperature difference alone.

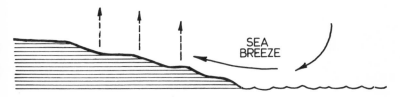

Air rises over the heating land and is replaced by air from over the colder sea, giving a sea breeze

Since the sea breeze owes its existence to the heating of land under a bright sun, it follows that it will die down as the sun sets. This is a most elementary forecasting fact which should be digested by the increasing band of enthusiasts who are taking to sailing. Don't get too far from base by late afternoon on a fine day or the exhilarating sail will turn into a wearying paddle.

At night, the calm resulting from the decease of a sea breeze may turn into a reverse off-land breeze if there is no blanket of cloud to prevent radiation cooling. The temperature of towpath will fall below that of river and the temperature of the shore will fall considerably below the temperature of the deep sea. The land breeze which sets in is not usually as strong as the daytime sea breeze but it is better than nothing for those dependent upon sail. It can be felt most effectively within a mile or two of shore, which should be borne in mind when navigating in apparently calm conditions.

Inland on clear nights, surface cooling serves to set up air movements wherever there are undulations of contour. As the air gets colder and heavier, it sinks as far as it can, settling into hollows, drifting down slopes and blowing quite appreciably down steep mountainsides. Such a wind is known as a katabatic wind. Wherever hills or mountains rise close to the shore line the katabatic effect adds considerably to the strength of the night-time land breeze.

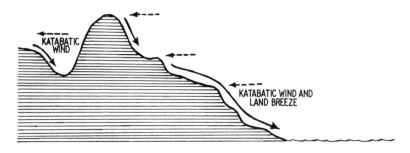

Air in contact with cooling land sinks as far as it can, causing a down-slope katabatic wind. When the sinking effect is added to the difference in temperature between land and sea at night, a land breeze can attain considerable strength

GLOBAL WINDS

On worldwide scale, the same principle of temperature difference operates to start the major wind systems. Large volumes of air rise over the equator creating a demand for colder air as replacement; large volumes of air over the polar regions, with their meagre ration of sunlight, are persistently colder than those at the equator. However, the very magnitude of these masses of air compared with the size of the world introduces complications which thwart a straightforward tendency for air to flow continually from polar to equatorial regions. For one thing, there are more accessible sources of replacement air nearer the equator. Even if equatorial seas seem to people in more northerly latitudes to be like hot baths, they are still considerably cooler than the adjacent land bathed in sunshine, and readily supply cooler air-flow on to land. And the basic tendency of the colder latitudes to supply warmer regions with cold air is mitigated by the fact that even in a northern summer the temperature of land areas may rise considerably above that of the seas which lap their shores— nothing dramatic, but relatively quite sufficient to cause air movements which are contrary to the fundamental polar-equatorial tendency.

Moreover, in considering these very large masses of air, we must remember that we are dealing not with a small parcel of reasonably homogenous temperature, but with a layer over 10 miles thick, and by no means of the same temperature throughout its depth.

VERTICAL TEMPERATURE DIFFERENCES

Because the basic mechanism for raising air temperature starts at ground level with heating of the surface by the sun, temperature is generally higher near the surface than further away. But variations are caused by local conditions and by slow mixing with airs 'imported' from other regions. Sometimes the rate of decrease of temperature with height is very fast, sometimes rather slow, sometimes air temperature may even increase with height for a short distance. On any one day, at any one place, air will have its particular temperature profile, and this is as unlikely to be identical with that on the day before or the day after as the finding of identical human profiles.

There is, moreover, another mechanism for raising air temperature which is independent of any source of radiating heat and which compensates for the gross favouritism towards the equatorial regions in the matter of sunshine. If air is compressed, its temperature will rise *for this reason alone*. This fact is familiar to anyone who has forced air through a bicycle pump and felt how hot it gets. Contrariwise, if the pressure on air is decreased, the air expands and its temperature falls. For instance, the sudden release of gas from a sparklet cartridge into a soda siphon makes that empty cartridge too cold to handle with comfort.

Similar pressure changes occur in our atmosphere. The thickness of air above us has weight and exerts a pressure which is generally unnoticed because it surrounds and penetrates every-thing, equalising inward and outward pressures. The greater the height one ventures to, the less the weight of air above. Pressure is less at the top of a hill than at the bottom, and very much less at the flying height of aircraft. The human frame is designed to cope with gradual variations in pressure, but rapid changes, even if quite small, can cause discomfort. Motoring down hills often results in blocked ears which can be cleared by swallowing hard. The rapid and large increase of pressure when descending from the heights at which modern aircraft fly is too great a strain on the human body and cabins have to be artificially pressurised to compensate.

In the atmosphere, changing pressure acts something like an equalising temperature tax. Any air moving for one reason or another downwards into a region of higher pressure gets a subsidy of rise in temperature; any air moving upwards into regions of lower pressure pays a tax of reduction in temperature. Moreover, tax and subsidy are levied at a known fixed rate (called the adiabatic lapse rate) and in all latitudes. For instance, very cold air sinking in polar regions gets a bonus temperature rise at some levels of its profile to make it on average warmer than it would otherwise be. Equatorial air pays a high tax in tem-perature reduction on all its volumes of light warmed air rising over its land, so that it has a lower average temperature than one might imagine.

Air which is cold at the surface may be relatively warm aloft; air which is warm at the surface may be relatively cold aloft; and what is what on any one day is ascertained by meteorologists by balloon and aircraft ascents with recording instruments, from strategically placed stations. The resulting three-dimensional puzzle of which air will flow in which direction because of temperature differences can, fortunately for the sanity of weather observers, be solved by measurements of atmospheric pressure in a horizontal plane. Whatever the vertical variations of temperature, the total thickness of air above any place will exert one pressure at the surface which can be measured. It will vary from place to place at any one moment of time. It can be high or low in winter or summer and in whatever latitude. But when all the readings of atmospheric pressure for one moment of time are plotted on a map they form patterns from which we can determine wind direction and strength and probable weather type. Pressure pattern is the most rewarding meteorological tool for the amateur, and much of the rest of this book will show how to use it.

CHAPTER FOUR

MEASUREMENT OF PRESSURE AND WIND

THE BAROMETER

The pressure exerted by the atmosphere at sea level is equivalent to that exerted by a column of mercury about 28-32in high. A convenient measure of pressure, therefore, is obtained by the distance mercury rises up a tube evacuated of air and inverted with the open end in a trough of mercury. The force which holds the mercury up the tube is the extra pressure of the air on the outside surface of mercury. Such an instrument is called a barometer. It can be made on the same principle using any other liquid, but mercury has the advantage of being very heavy, about thirty times heavier than water, so that a comparatively small height will balance the atmospheric pressure. A barometer consisting of a water column would need to be about 960in high—a bit cumbersome!

Though mercury barometers are still used for precision work, they need careful handling and are not easily portable. So there has evolved the aneroid barometer, basically a box supported by an internal spring and almost evacuated of air, which concertinas according to the air pressure acting on its outer side (see p 32). Fluctuations are registered by a pointer moving over a

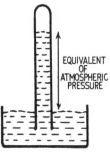

Atmospheric pressure on the free surface of a mercury barometer balances the extra column of mercury in the tube, which is evacuated of air

dial face. Nearly all domestic barometers nowadays are of this type, and many antique barometer cases have had aneroid mechanisms substituted for mercury. A barograph is a barometer which records variations in pressure; an ink nib attached to its pointer traces a fluctuating line on a chart fixed to a rotating drum (pp 154, 156-7).

Many instruments still record pressure in terms of inches or millimetres of mercury. However, the international unit used in all forecasting work is the millibar, which is the equivalent unit of force. In these terms, atmospheric pressure ranges between about 940mb, very low, and 1050mb, very high—variations between 980 and 1030mb being more common. Since many barometer faces carry two scales, a traditional prejudice for length of mercury can be happily combined with a millibar scale for convenient use of published and broadcast material.

To determine the worldwide pattern of pressure it is necessary to have a regular and plentiful supply of barometric readings. Over the last hundred years, co-operation among meteorologists of many countries has gradually resulted in an international system of weather reporting (including pressure levels) at fixed time intervals. Since patterns of pressure only make sense if readings are made at the same time everywhere, weather offices all over the world are geared internally to Greenwich Mean Time.

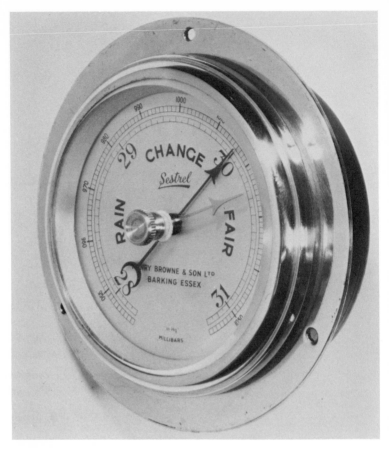

Aneroid barometer, scale in inches and millibars, suitable for a yacht

In order to isolate the pattern of pressure which determines weather, irregularities which are caused solely by the physical contours of the land are 'ironed out' by correcting to mean sea level. If a pressure reading is taken on a hill, then the pressure of an imaginary column of air the same height as the hill and at the current temperature is added to the reading. This involves something like 1mb for every 30ft above sea level.

ISOBARS

A tabulated list of pressures makes as little impact on the mind as does a tabulated list of topographical heights. Geographers plot height readings on to maps, join up those of equal value and call them contour lines. The closer the spacing of consecutive contours, the steeper is the gradient of the ground enclosed. Such a map tells us more than any verbose description. In effect, the map gives the eye long-range vision.

Meteorologists do the same with pressure readings. They plot them on maps, join those having equal value (usually at 2mb or 4mb intervals) and call them isobars. The closer the isobars, the steeper the pressure gradient and the faster will air flow because of it. By definition, no one isobar can cross another and the lines are closed circuits.

On normal fluid principles, one would expect winds caused by atmospheric pressure differences to flow direct from high pressure to low pressure. Because of the dimensions involved, however, the fact that the earth is itself rotating beneath the moving air causes an apparent deflection of the wind to the right in the northern hemisphere, to the left in the southern hemisphere. The deflection resolves itself into a neat 90° at 2000ft above surface level, which is the height considered to be beyond the influence of drag due to surface friction. Wind speed and direction is related to the isobars by the following rule, which should be memorised as an essential and simple tool for weather inter-pretation. The fact that this book does not delve into the reasons *why* it is so, in no way diminishes its use to the layman.

> The wind at 2000ft above the ground blows parallel to the isobars, so that when it is visualised as blowing on one's back the centre of low pressure is on the left hand in the northern hemisphere.
>
> The closer the isobars, the stronger the wind speed.

33

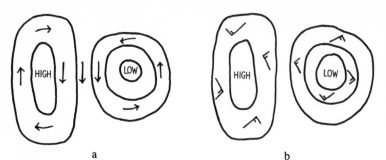

(a) The wind at 2000ft above ground blows parallel to the isobars. If you imagine it as blowing on the back, then low pressure is on the left hand. Direction is given by arrow heads. (b) Surface wind blows more closely to the basic high-to-low direction, that is inwards to the centre of low pressure and outwards from the centre of high pressure. Direction is given by arrow shafts, each half-barb representing about 5 mph

WIND NOTATION

Consider now the simplest pressure pattern, showing closed isobars round a centre of low pressure and a centre of high pressure. Applying the above wind rule (northern hemisphere) you will see that at 2000ft the wind must blow anticlockwise round the low pressure centre and clockwise round the high. Only in this way can back be to wind and low pressure on the left. (The isobaric chart is a plan view, seen from above.) In the southern hemisphere the directions are reversed.

At surface level, wind tends to cling to the ground because of friction, and the deflection from the basic tendency of high-to-low pressure is not so great. Consequently, surface wind blows a bit more towards the centre of low pressure than does the wind at 2000ft. Over the sea there is less surface friction and the surface wind will have only a slight deviation in direction from that at 2000ft. As regards strength, the same drag of ground friction causes surface wind to be somewhat less strong than that at 2000ft.

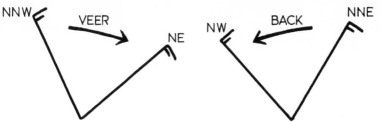

Wind veers if it changes in a clockwise direction, backs if it changes in an anticlockwise direction

Wind direction is always given as the direction *from which* it blows. For instance, a NW wind comes from the north-west and blows towards the south-east. If wind direction changes in the same direction as the hands of a clock, it is said to *veer*. If it changes in the opposite direction it is said to *back*. On a chart the surface wind direction is marked by a line from the point of origin towards the station where it is recorded. The strength is shown by the number of barbs, each half-barb being about 5mph.

Study again the isobaric pattern illustrated, and you will see that because of the greater high-to-low tendency of surface wind, it is always *backed* from the direction of the wind at 2000ft given by the isobars. The amount involved is in the region of 10° over the sea and can be about 30° over land.

ISOBARIC CHARTS

An isobaric chart differs from a geographical contour map in two special ways apart from the units recorded. First, it is bound to be slightly out of date before it is even completed. There is a time lapse between making pressure readings and receiving them at weather centres; they take time to plot and the isobars take time to draw. During this time the weather has also been changing. A local chart for one country alone may be completed in an hour, but one covering the whole world probably requires several hours before all parts of the jigsaw are completed. Nevertheless, the charts are most efficient tools for forecasting, and techno-logical improvements in communication will undoubtedly continue to reduce the time lag even if unable to eliminate it.

In compensation for the time delay and the need for perpetually making new charts to keep pace with the weather, isobaric charts can be drawn with far fewer readings than are necessary for a geographical contour map. This is because pressure levels generally change smoothly, so that it is possible to interpolate between known values with considerable confidence of accuracy. If, for instance, two reporting stations several miles apart with the same wind direction and strength, have pressure readings of 1000mb and 1004mb, it is safe to infer that a place midway between will have a pressure of 1002mb. If the wind were stronger at the station with the 1000mb reading, then the 1002mb isobar would be closer to that station than to the other. If the weather and wind direction were different at the two stations, it is still possible to infer the intervening isobars according to certain rules which will be dealt with later. A perfectly adequate chart for a country the size of the British Isles can be drawn by the layman with about a dozen pressure readings broadcast in a few moments over the air.

CHAPTER FIVE

WATER IN THE AIR

The component of the atmosphere which gives us our major weather troubles is water, which may take the guise of invisible vapour or visible drops. There is always water vapour present in the air, either indoors or out, either on a cloudy day or a sunny one; more obviously, there is water in the air on a foggy day or a rainy one. The visible water drops have been conjured out of clear air, and it is essential for understanding weather to be absolutely certain how this happens. Since air and water vapour are invisible, it is helpful to make explanations in terms of familiar tangible objects.

CONDENSATION

Imagine the air around you to be a beaker the height of which is proportional to the temperature of the air. You know it contains water though this cannot be seen. Suppose next that something happens to reduce the height of the beaker. A small reduction may still leave the water safely hidden in the beaker, continual reduction will eventually bring the side level with the water. After this point, any further reduction in height of the side will cause the contents to spill out, as shown over, most visibly wet.

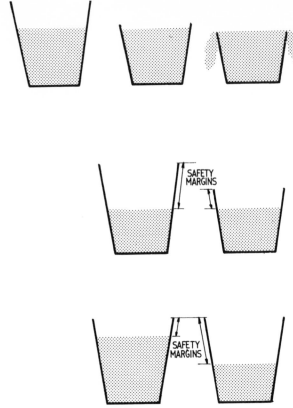

(a) *Water eventually spills out of a beaker as the sides are cut down.* (b) *Given the same contents, the larger beaker has a higher safety margin than the smaller.* (c) *Given the same size beaker, the emptier beaker has a higher safety margin than the fuller*

Given exactly the same *contents*, the taller the beaker to start with, the further the sides can be cut down without accident (above).

Given exactly the same size *beakers*, the fuller one will have an accident first if the sides of the two are pared down equally (above).

Translating back into terms of air and temperature, all air contains water vapour of varying quantities. The lower the air temperature, the smaller the maximum possible capacity for vapour. If something happens to lower temperature beyond the level, called dew point, where vapour content is the maximum possible, then condensation will occur. A jug of iced water taken from the refrigerator into a warm room will collect drops of condensation as the air cools over its surface. The same principle governs the formation of dew, mist, fog, cloud or rain. Cooling, however it happens, is the villain of the whole weather story. If dew point is below freezing level, condensation will be directly into ice crystals, commonly called hoar frost.

Since condensation is not a matter of one particular temperature but of a difference between two, the phenomenon occurs at all times of the year and in all parts of the world. Clouds, rain and fog can as well occur when summer air cools as when winter air cools, providing the humidity characteristics are about the same. At certain times of the year and in various parts of the world, humidity and cooling factors are accentuated so as to make bad weather more likely, but it is all a matter of proportion. Any weather wisdom learnt in one's own home town can be applied with little effort when on holiday elsewhere, either in the same country or abroad, by assessing the relative importance of local factors.

The non-seasonal aspects of condensation can be illustrated by the miniature problems of weather inside a car. The modern luxury of heaters and tight-fitting windows allow us to build up very snug atmospheres inside cars in winter, with temperatures appreciably higher than outside. Add a few occupants exhaling moisture, and humidity rises too. If this moist warm air is allowed to linger on cold windows it will condense and impede visibility. The solution is either to keep air on the move, by a fan on the windscreen or with a through air-flow ventilation system, so that it will not have time to cool against the windows, or to heat windows electrically so that it doesn't matter if air does linger because it won't cool as far as condensation level.

In summer, heaters are not used and the temperature difference between inside and out is not great. Humidity may be high, but problems of condensation can usually be solved comfortably when on the move by opening a window to secure circulation of air. But imagine a picnic on a warm day suddenly interrupted by a shower, and a mad rush of persons to the shelter of the parked car. Because of the shower *outside*, the car is suddenly cooled and because of the panting warm persons *inside*, temperature and humidity are abruptly raised. If windows are closed against the rain there will be heavy condensation on them, and even opening a window will hardly help if the car is stationary.

In sub-freezing weather, condensation inside car or house windows may freeze into fern-like patterns of ice crystals. The most dramatic display I have ever seen was made by an anxious dog peering after me and breathing heavily on the window. It needed only a few moments of this very humid air on the icy window to render it unserviceable for seeing through.

EVAPORATION

The domestic economy of the universe dictates that nothing shall be wasted. Therefore a convenient mechanism exists by which water that is spilled out from air as it cools can be retrieved, either when temperature rises again or when a drier airstream follows. This is evaporation. Dew disperses when the sun raises temperature next morning, puddles evaporate in the dry air which follows a shower, and rain which fills lakes, rivers and seas provides a perpetual drinking trough for thirsty airs. It is an endless economical merry-go-round of give and take, with basically one universal supply of water.

Since air has this thirst for water if not already full to vapour capacity, it follows that the air streams of significantly high humidities are those which have had plenty of opportunity to drink, that is those that have had a long journey across the sea.

These air streams respond most rapidly to the processes of cooling which lead to weather deterioration. The very dry air streams are those which have travelled across continents, without access to large expanses of water. Such airs can endure considerable cooling before needing to shed vapour as condensation, but are particularly greedy for any little source of water they can find. Washing on the line dries in a twinkling, hoed weeds shrivel rapidly and when surface soil has been robbed of its moisture content the probing air seeks even further down. If evaporation reaches to root level, plants wilt rapidly.

Evaporation can cause indoor weather problems as a consequence of modern central heating and double glazing of windows. Constantly warm temperatures increase the vapour capacity of rooms considerably and containers of water placed near radiators only partially help redress the balance. In Britain, where stoical endurance of windows wide open to the moist island climate is only now succumbing to the winter comforts Americans have had for years, old furniture can suffer. Hidden reserves of moisture are surrendered to the dry air and shrinkage can result in irreparable damage. Too late I discovered a crack in an antique cupboard of mine. I have arrested, and possibly partly corrected, the damage by keeping a bowl of water inside. The rate at which the water evaporates makes me think the crack would never have occurred if I had done this on first bringing the cupboard from its original home and putting it near a radiator.

Plants take up water through the root system and transpire it again through the pores of leaves. In the dry atmosphere of a heated house the rate of transpiration will be rapid and supply through the stem may not keep pace. Spraying foliage with water may be necessary as well as soil watering, and this is specially true for greenhouses in high summer. The advice of experts should always be taken on the favourite temperature and humidity conditions of any plants one wants to grow.

Inside home or greenhouse we can, within limits, act as all-powerful makers of weather, but we can have only one type at a time. Outside there is enough room for many weathers to exist side by side, and natural production methods are on a correspondingly large scale. The sun is the prime heating element which raises temperature and increases the vapour capacity of air, hastening the transformation of water back into vapour state. We must now consider the natural cooling methods which lower temperature, bring air to condensation level and thereby produce all the wet phenomena which are both the nuisance and the lifeblood of our existence.

CHAPTER SIX

COOLING BY CONTACT—DEW

The simplest cooling method is by contact with a colder surface, and I suppose one of the first weather lessons we unconsciously learn as children is about radiation cooling at sunset. Those wretched cardigans we always had to carry on the hottest of picnics, but which were usually most welcome on the chilly journey home!

RADIATION COOLING

When the sun sets, the earth and any other radiating object upon it (car, roofs, blades of grass, etc) continue to radiate heat from their own modest supplies and at varying rates according to the substances of which they are made. With no heat from the sun to replenish their stocks, temperatures fall.

Maximum loss of heat occurs when there is no overhead shelter to prevent escape into the atmosphere. Houses, tents and sacking are obvious examples of covers that help to prevent heat loss, but branches of trees, even when leafless, give some shelter to the ground below, and a wire mesh netting is better than nothing at all. The biggest single deterrent to the formation of the weather phenomena associated with radiation cooling is a blanket of cloud. Heat radiated from the earth is of the long-wave variety and this is readily absorbed by the water drops of clouds, which in turn reflect some of the heat back again to earth. If there is a complete cover of cloud all night, there is unlikely to be any dramatic change in weather because of ground cooling alone. If there is a clear sky all night, radiation cooling can result in sudden weather deterioration.

TEMPERATURE INVERSION

As surface temperature falls under a clear sky, so does that of the air in immediate contact with the surface. Very slowly this fall is transmitted from the lowest layer to the one above, while the temperature nearest the cooling surface falls still lower. Eventually surface air temperature will become low enough to condense out water vapour as dew. The normal temperature profile of the air above (that is, temperature decrease with height) becomes inverted and temperatures actually rise with height for a while before reverting to their usual tendency to fall. If there is no wind and the ground is level, the cold air will squat stolidly near the surface and there will be a large temperature difference between this air and that at a few feet above the ground. Condensation as dew will occur long before the air above is saturated with vapour.

RADIATION DEW

Radiation dew occurs all through the year, even in summer, and forms more rapidly on some surfaces than on others. A parked car, being made of materials which lose heat rapidly and having no inner warmth to draw upon, cools quickly at night. It is soon covered with dew if air is calm enough to linger long on its surface. Dew forms first on roof, boot and bonnet because they are exposed to radiation loss under the full sky and are horizontal enough to allow the cooling air to settle without draining off. Front and rear windscreens which slope outwards from top to bottom collect dew before vertical side windows, from which air tends to sink to the ground. The *inward* sloping rear window of some older cars hardly ever collected dew at all because the slight overhang of roof protected against radiation loss.

There is little one can do to prevent dew forming on a parked car, short of putting a cover over it to insulate against heat loss and to take any dew deposit. Parking close to a house wall helps a lot because the car is exposed to a smaller area of open sky. The windows nearest the wall may still be quite dry the following morning while those on the further side are well covered in dew.

The roadway on which a car is standing may remain dry all night under a clear sky because it cools at a slower rate than metal, and also because some heat from deeper down in the subsoil may have been conducted to the surface to counteract temperature fall. Likewise in a garden the bare soil surface will benefit from conduction of heat from the subsoil, specially if that is moist, and soil temperature may remain well above dew point while the adjacent lawn is dripping with water drops.

Dew forms along the flat surfaces of grass blades. Guttation drops cling to the tips

There are two reasons why grass and low-lying compact plants get so wet at night even in summer. Heat is radiated from the upper surface of blades or leaves, and stored heat from the subsoil is conducted to the base of stems. Between top and bottom is an efficient insulating barrier of stems and air spaces which prevents this emergency ration of heat being used to equalise temperature. Moreover, plants themselves transpire vapour, which means that in the lilliputian jungle of blades of grass there is a perpetual moist atmosphere. Almost any clear still night will give cooling to dew point over grass. Small beads of dew form along the flat radiating surfaces of the blades, and single large drops of transpired water, called guttation, cling to the tips, unable to evaporate because the air is saturated (see p 45). The more finely cut and closely packed the grass, the better the insulation and the more spectacular the display of dew and guttation. When I exercise my dog in the early morning on the local recreation ground the grass is unevenly wet, the thin scuffed patches being almost dry because subsoil heat has had a chance to get at it. The adjacent bowling greens are a blinding display of sunlight reflected from a myriad drops.

Though dew may seem too commonplace to warrant classification as weather, it does have considerable importance in the miniature climates of lawns. For though temperatures may fall far at grass level on a summer night, the lowest level is still relatively warm and moist, and these conditions are favourable for the spread of certain fungi. The bowling-green keeper is continually on the alert for signs of trouble as he drags the green with a special mat first thing in the morning to hasten drying (p 47).

I do not suggest that we should start regarding dew with apprehension. That would make garden hypochondriacs of us all in no time. But dew can be a useful weather clue. Sometimes we are confronted in the early morning with a formless cloud cover which it is hard to analyse. The state of the ground can indicate how long it has been in existence. If the lawns are wet with dew but the paths dry, then the cloud cover has probably only recently

Heavy dew forms over closely cut and compact grass during still, cloudless nights—the net is used to hasten drying in the morning

formed; if both paths and lawns are dry the cloud has probably been there most of the night, preventing radiation cooling; if both lawns and paths are wet then the cloud has probably been giving rain.

Wind is the best preventative of radiation dew formation under a clear sky, by preventing air lingering on a surface long enough to cool to dew point. Hence even heavy dew on a parked car is not a great problem to motorists. It must be cleaned off before driving away, but once the car is moving it creates its own air flow to prevent re-formation.

ADVECTION DEW

The one occasion when wind does not deter condensation is at the rapid collapse of a cold winter spell. Unheated buildings or rooms and their contents may be extremely cold, and suddenly a swing of wind, often to the south-west, brings moist air and a temperature rise of perhaps 5-10°C in an hour or so. This new air stream takes time to penetrate closed buildings and even longer to raise the temperature of things inside. On its first contact with cold surfaces the warmer air causes furniture to bloom over and walls run with condensation even to the extent of peeling off wallpaper. At the first warning in a weather forecast that mild weather is approaching, rooms that have been closed up during the cold spell to conserve heat should be re-opened and treated to a little artificial heating. If the contents are already warm when the new air arrives damage will be minimised.

If warm air arrives unexpectedly, motorists should have the forethought to get cars out of unheated garages at least a quarter of an hour before needed to give them a chance to acclimatise. Because the difference in temperature between car and air is a condition of the whole air mass, not just the thin skin in contact with the car, condensation will persist even when the car is moving. Till the car has taken up the new warm temperature it is a waste of time trying to wipe windows clean because they will mist up again immediately.

SUPERCOOLED DEW

Water drops have a disconcerting property of being able to flout the rule about freezing at 0°C. Ice will always melt at that temperature but water drops will not always freeze. At very low pressures they can exist in liquid state to temperatures even as low as −40°C, but at normal atmospheric pressures −5°C is a more usual limit.

Supercooling is an extremely fickle condition and the slightest pressure or contact with freezing objects will cause the drops to transform to ice. In cold weather dew often forms on windows at a temperature just above 0°C and the drops remain liquid for a while when temperature continues to fall below 0°C. If you then try and wipe the window clean in order to see through it better the situation is made worse by the drops freezing into an opaque crust of ice. Alternatively, some hoar frost crystals may form after the temperature has fallen below 0°C and these will set off a chain reaction throughout the supercooled drops, each drop freezing on contact with the adjacent ice till beautiful fern patterns cover the area.

CHAPTER SEVEN

COOLING BY CONTACT—FROST

HOAR FROST AND AIR FROST

With whatever equanimity we regard radiation dew, we cannot afford to be complacent about its winter counterpart, hoar frost. This forms as a result of radiation cooling when dew point is reached and is below 0°C. Condensation occurs directly as a crust of white ice crystals, a picturesque condition (opposite) which is rightly dreaded because of the damage that follows. But it is hardly fair to put all the blame upon the crystals which are merely one particular and visible symptom of freezing conditions. If dew point is well below 0°C, air temperature can be below freezing yet above dew point and no hoar frost will form. This condition is called air frost and since it causes water to freeze and expand, it does the same ugly damage to plants, car radiators or outside water pipes, as if it were accompanied by hoar frost.

Air frost can occur without hoar frost, but hoar frost implies at any rate a thin layer of air frost near the cooling surface. In very cold spells there can be hoar frost on the ground and air frost for quite a distance above the ground. On more fortunate occasions, hoar frost may cover the ground while temperatures at tree-branch level remain above 0°C—a lucky escape for fruit blossom.

Hoar frost and rime during prolonged cold spell

CONDITIONS FOR FROST FORMATION

Since frost forms in exactly the same way as radiation dew, the same conditions govern its formation. Greatest risk is when sky is clear, wind still, nights long and the air stream of cold origin so that dusk temperature is already low. Meteorologists have formulae with which to gauge frost risk, and to their general warning the layman must add or subtract the peculiarities of particular localities.

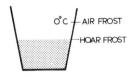

Air frost can occur without hoar frost if dew-point temperature is below 0° C

Since cooling air will always drain downhill if possible, valleys have greatest risk, hilltops least. But remember that even on a hilltop there can be hollows or depressions which become frost traps.

Coastal areas benefit from the moderating influence of the sea; land breezes draw off the cooling air and prevent temperature falling too low over land.

In the northern hemisphere southern areas have shorter nights than northern areas, and therefore suffer less night-time cooling. Southern areas also have a slightly higher sun altitude and may start the night with a higher temperature than northern areas if the sun has been shining.

The arithmetic of all these factors adds up to just the sort of frost map for the British Isles that one would expect. The greatest frost frequency is in Scotland and in low-lying central areas elsewhere, from the beginning of September through winter till the beginning of June. The lowest frequency is in the south and in coastal areas, with a few favoured tips of south-west England, Ireland and Wales where frost hardly ever occurs. It is in these areas that the early vegetable market has naturally developed.

FORECASTING FROST

Commercial growers, power stations, building contractors and other enterprises which have much at stake on a small variation in temperature at low levels, can avail themselves of telegraphed frost-warning systems run by most meteorological offices.

The ordinary householder, motorist or gardener can probably avert most troubles by recognising potentially dangerous situations and playing for safety. Antifreeze to lower the freezing point of water in car radiators should be used at any rate by the end of September in the British Isles, and any still clear dusk around this time be taken as a warning to adopt frost precautions. Such dusks often follow still sunny days when temperatures build up to the illusion of high summer. Don't be lulled into a false sense of security; the calendar does not lie to that extent.

The amateur who is particularly interested in forecasting radiation frost during the critical spring months March-May, may like to try a method devised by L. P. Smith of the Meteorological Office. It requires the use of thermometers and the making of a weather observation each evening, but is not difficult and has had considerable success (see Appendix, p 168).

However technical or non-technical the approach, it is important to remember that *all* the factors involved—sky, wind and temperature—must be considered when trying to evaluate frost risk. Any method which purports to predict frost on dusk temperatures alone cannot tell the whole story.

The moon, however, is *not* one of the factors concerned, except indirectly as an aid to observation. There is at present no proof that the moon has any causative effect on weather, though those who believe some connection exists may one day be able to produce enough evidence to stand the scrutiny of scientific investigation. The moon's overwhelming contribution to the art of weather forecasting is simply in getting people to look at the sky. An unclouded full moon is so dramatic, a new moon so dainty, that the eye is inevitably drawn towards it. When it can be seen, it means no intervening cloud exists and this, not the moon itself, is what should be a warning of frost. The moon is still there even if it is obscured by cloud. For those who like rhyming folk lore, I suggest changing the phrase, 'Full moon, frost soon' to one which better indicates the causative factor. What about 'Clear sky, frost nigh'?

PRECAUTIONS

The only reason for wanting to anticipate frost formation is to avert the unpleasant consequences. If it appears that natural conditions of wind, cloud or warmth are not going to protect against it, we must try and provide the equivalent ourselves.

Artificial cover is the best hope. If a car cannot be inside a garage, then park it under a tree or close to a wall so that it is exposed to a smaller area of open sky and frost formation may be delayed. Windows nearest the wall may escape frost altogether while outside windows get covered. A covering of cloth or newspaper on the screen will protect additionally by providing an insulating air space and giving an alternative surface for the frost to form over. If screens do get frosted, they can be fairly easily scraped clean with a plastic-edged tool. The thing *not* to attempt is to clear with a wet cloth. This merely adds more water to freeze on the cold screen, and solid ice is much harder to get off than crystalline frost.

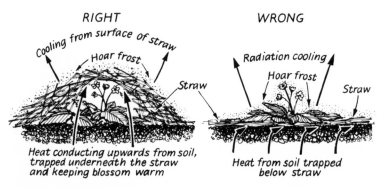

Protective material must cover the whole *plant if it is to give benefit against frost*

In the garden, small plants can be covered with paper cones, inverted flower pots, straw or evergreen twigs to take the brunt of the cooling and give the plant beneath an insulating layer of warmer air. None of these on their own will protect against a frost of long duration, but against the short-term frost, particularly in the critical spring period, they can be adequate. Whatever is used must cover the *whole* plant if it is to be effective. If straw is simply laid around the base of fruit bushes, radiation heat loss will occur above the covering and critically lower the air temperature for young shoots and blossom; conducted heat from the subsoil will be prevented by the insulating material from counteracting the danger. With or without cover, low plants can be additionally protected if soil is well watered during the day. This will improve the conductivity of heat to the surface, possibly enough to prevent a slight frost.

Temporary covers against night frost should be placed in position well before sunset, before daytime heat has had a chance to disperse. They should be taken off again after sun-up to allow further warmth from the sun to be put into store. 'On and off,' in the same way as clothing, is the best method of covering plants.

GLASS AS PROTECTION

A special word must be said about the role of glass as a protective substance. Heat radiated from the sun is of very short wavelength, that radiated from the earth is long-wave. The peculiarity of glass is that it is readily transparent to short waves but not to long. Sunshine comes straight through glass to heat whatever is underneath, while heat re-radiated back again from such contents only passes very slowly back through glass by conduction. The 'greenhouse effect', therefore, is to give a cumulative build-up of temperature under glass during the day, which, in the warmer months of the year, can soon become excessive. Always make provision for good ventilation in greenhouse or cold frames on sunny days. More important still, never leave a child or dog unattended in a closed car in sunshine, even if a blowing wind makes the air outside seem quite cool.

LARGE-SCALE PROTECTION

Commercial growers have a problem when it comes to protecting an acreage of fruit or crops. They have experimented with fires to raise temperatures and smoke to blanket blossom, but heat is expensive to generate and easily dissipated, and smoke is an inefficient blanket against heat loss. Huge fans to keep air moving are a theoretical possibility but expensive and impractical to operate. So growers, too, turn to insulating cover. Page 57 shows an orange grove at Sorrento effectively protected by a simple method. One recent interesting development is a highly blown-up mixture of air, water and some secret chemical ingredient which sits lightly enough on plants to do no damage and disperses about twenty-four hours after application.

Californian fruit growers are having considerable success with artificially created fog. Overhead pipes carry water which is forced under pressure through a series of very fine nozzles along its length, producing small enough water drops to remain suspended in the air for a considerable time. Such a fog is merely cloud on the ground and effectively blankets the vital area against radiation heat loss.

FROST PALLIATIVE

A palliative, once freezing level is reached, is to spray plants with a very fine jet of water. The water freezes and cocoons the plants in ice, but the freezing process itself liberates a minute amount of heat, called latent heat, which is enough to counteract any further fall in temperature and possibly avert serious damage. Provided one can keep a mixture of ice and water over the plant the temperature will remain at $0°C$, but once there is ice *only* over the plant any further radiation heat loss will be reflected in further falls in temperature which a plant may not be able to bear. The

Reed matting overhead protects this orange grove at Sorrento from frost caused by radiation cooling. The semi-permeable reed palisade acts as a windbreak

spray of water must be very fine, otherwise damage by sheer weight of ice will be as great as it would have been by frost. It is a tricky operation which is not likely to be of more than academic interest to the layman, but it does illustrate another peculiarity of water's behaviour when subjected to cooling beyond o°C.

LIMIT TO PROTECTION

There is a limit to the protection that can be given outdoors against frost, and the sensible thing is only to attempt what is reasonably certain of success. For anyone wanting to tie up money in fruit or crops, it is worth while spending a bit more to make a thorough investigation into the weather characteristics of a particular site before starting. Householders, too, should resist pushing their luck too far with jobs which can spoil with frost. A concrete garden path laid on a fine autumn afternoon can be ruined by dawn if frost occurs and expands the still wet mixture; and new paint on an outside door can be spoiled if frost gets underneath before it is properly dry. Moreover, some synthetic varnishes will never set properly once temperatures fall below a certain point and much wasted labour goes into scraping off spoiled varnish or polyurethane. This seems to be a rather frequent predicament in the boating fraternity. In the last-minute rush to get boats ready for the water by Easter, fine spring days generate a mad activity, but the temptation to apply a last coat of varnish while the light lasts is one to be resisted if there is any suspicion that frost may occur during the night.

FROST AS A LABOUR SAVER

After such a tale of warning about frost, it is pleasant to record that it has its uses and can be a labour saver in the garden. When soil is dug over during the autumn it can be left in large clods without wasting effort to break it down to a fine tilth. Once a hard frost gets into it, the expanding water content forces the soil particles apart. When the frost is over, a light touch of rake or hoe and the job is done. Similarly, some of the most tiresome hand-weeding chores can be done most easily after an autumn ground frost which clears next morning. The expansion of the water will have half lifted shallow roots out of the ground and all that is necessary is to shake off loose soil.

ADVECTION FROST

Frost does not only occur when manufactured on the spot by radiation cooling. It can be imported, having been cooled by contact with a cold surface somewhere else and arriving in the wind. It will then cause everything else it envelops to take up gradually its own sub-freezing temperature. If local objects then cool still further at night by radiation cooling, home-produced hoar frost is added to imported air frost. Imported air frost, or advection frost, has all the characteristics of radiation frost, with the additional misery that it often lasts much longer. If it is accompanied by cloud, as often happens, there will be no amelioration of temperature during the day.

CHAPTER EIGHT

COOLING BY CONTACT—FOG

RADIATION FOG

I have shown that dew forms easily over grass because the thin layer of air next to it is always moist. Sometimes a much thicker layer of air may be moist and then condensation can occur throughout, giving fog. With no wind at all, fog will form first as shallow streaks near the ground, but absolute calm rarely exists in fact; there are always slopes down which cold air is draining, and this initiates movements of air from elsewhere which have to surmount or by-pass obstacles en route. If such slight turbulence is increased by a pressure wind of 4 or 5mph, cooling may spread evenly within a few hundred feet of the ground, shallow enough still to allow appreciable falls in temperature. When air is moist, cooling will soon lower temperature to dew point and fog will form, remaining below the top of the inversion level because of buoyancy principles (opposite). Whenever you see cows standing in a pool of evening mist you can be quite sure their feet are colder than their heads! And you can climb a hill out of thick fog to see chimneys and church spires sticking up through what looks like a sea of cotton wool, and know that you are warmer than those below.

Mist clings to the ground under an inversion of temperature; warmer above the mist than below

FACTORS CONTRIBUTING TO FOG

Air may be moist because it has had a long sea track before arrival. In addition there may be local sources of water such as river, lake and marsh ground; or normally dry ground may be wet because a shower has fallen. All these factors increase the likelihood of fog under clear night skies. Towns have certain peculiarities of their own. Artificial sources of heat make them slightly warmer than open country, which somewhat delays cooling to dew point. To set against this advantage, they have plenty of dirt particles in the air and these serve as accommodating nucleii for condensation and encourage fog.

As with frost risk, so with fog. Formation is most likely in low-lying ground and hollows, least likely on the top of hills. A general appraisal of fog risk by a meteorological office is based on average characteristics of the air mass and the cooling expected, but it cannot possibly add the detail for every locality. The individual must tailor the forecast to suit, emphasising the forecast risk for a low-lying river valley, but possibly minimising the risk for a dry hill top. Once fog has formed within an area, it can make all the difference to a motoring journey if the route can be planned to avoid known fog traps.

CLEARANCE

Apart from any radical change in weather system, clearance of fog may be achieved next day by heating from the sun. Timing of clearance requires more information than the layman has at his disposal, but an estimate can always be got from the weather office. Broadly speaking, summer radiation fog, which is rare, clears by breakfast; fog in late spring and early autumn disperses by mid-morning, but in early spring and late autumn probably lifts only briefly around midday before re-forming again. In settled spells, when fog forms regularly at night, clearance often occurs at about the same time on consecutive days and it is worth watching for such periodicity. During the process of stirring up and dispersal of fog, hill tops which have remained above fog all night may become temporarily engulfed before the whole lot finally dissipates.

In winter the position is bleak. With much more cooling at night than heating by day, the puny sun may make no impression on fog at all. It can persist for days, till one feels suffocated by the white nothingness pressing against the windows. The sensation can become dreadful reality for the old and ill, for chemicals produced from coal fires and industrial plants dissolve in the fog to form acids and produce lethal 'smog'. This new word was coined in December 1952 when four days of continuous fog in Britain claimed a heavy death toll and gave the necessary jolt to complacency about air pollution. The subsequent introduction of smokeless zones has already had a marked effect in decreasing the incidence of smog, and with luck future generations may have to ask what smog or a yellow pea-souper was.

Even in winter, fog must clear some time. It can happen when another weather system advances, bringing drier air and stronger wind; weather maps give good indication of such a change. On other occasions the weather situation may remain basically the same, but a slight increase in wind to about 10mph may lift fog right off the ground to give a formless sheet of very low cloud. This is called stratus and, like fog, it will sit underneath the upper temperature inversion. Such small wind increases when pressure gradient is already slack are often a matter of chance and almost impossible to predict. It is important to appreciate this inherent imprecision if relations between official forecasters and the public are not to turn sour. Meteorologically there is hardly any change in weather situation, but of course for traffic the change is absolute, from complete paralysis to freedom of movement. It is understandable that the public urgently requires to know *when* clearance will happen, but it is not negligence that fails to produce the right answer. Angry questions asked in Parliament or letters in the press demanding vengeance cannot achieve what is at the moment impossible.

PATCHINESS OF FOG

There is only a degree of temperature or a percentage of humidity difference between clear air and fog, and because conditions over different surfaces are never exactly the same, there is a transition period between a fine night and totally obscuring fog which is characterised by drifting patches of fog. However small a patch of fog it can have the effect of a blindfold on a motorist, quite frightening in contrast to normal unimpaired vision. He can be driving at a fair speed with everything visible ahead and the next moment be enveloped in fog. Out again into starlight, and fog can be dismissed as a freak patch till he is suddenly enveloped once again. Once in that patch he may have to drop down to crawling pace and if the car following does not, there is an accident. The same patchiness occurs during clearance and the rapid alternation between sunlight and fog is every bit as dangerous to the motorist as patchiness at night.

This is part of the problem of 'motorway madness'. As I go to search the records for details of the last pile-up of 70 cars, sickeningly my quest is no longer necessary. The television is pouring out details of another pile-up: 130 vehicles involved, 9 dead and 50 injured, and people interviewed expressing surprise that a patch of fog could so abruptly curtail vision. We must stop being surprised and understand the enemy we are up against. Patchiness is the nature of the beast; no one can predict where each patch will form, nor is each patch always visible more than a few yards ahead.

PROTECTION AFFORDED BY FOG

There is one crumb of comfort among the miseries of fog. It does provide a protection against further falls in temperature and may therefore be welcomed by gardeners and growers as an alternative to frost. In the British Isles, the moist air streams which are most prone to condensation on cooling are also the mild ones from the Atlantic which have a relatively high temperature at dusk and consequently are not frost prone. But with the colder air streams from some northerly point or perhaps even from west or east, dusk temperatures in spring and autumn can be fairly low. These airs are usually relatively dry and much cooling can take place before condensation occurs, by which time freezing level may well be reached. It can be a saving grace on such an evening if dusk showers leave surface air wet so that fog forms. Even if only temporary, it may prevent frost forming.

SUPERCOOLED FOG

There are unpleasant occasions when an airstream reaching Britain in winter may be below freezing level and also moist, for instance if air has come from Scandinavia and had a long track down the North Sea. This can produce fog of supercooled water drops, and as these drift past cold objects they freeze, covering the world with a white crust of rime. This looks something like hoar frost in that it is a loosely packed ice crust, but the individual particles are frozen drops, looking like pellets, and not crystals as when precipitated directly from the vapour state. Rime builds up on the windward side of obstacles, often to considerable thickness (p 51).

ADVECTION FOG

The fall in temperature necessary to induce fog formation is achieved not only by contact with a surface which is itself cooling by radiation, but also by passage over a surface which cools gradually or abruptly according to geographical position. This is called 'advection fog'. The sudden arrival of moist warm air over a land covered with snow or hard with frost will cause fog to form, in the same way that dew forms over a cold car. Because the whole air mass has such different temperature from the surface over which it is passing, fog will form even if quite a strong wind is blowing, and will not disperse till the ground itself warms and thaws under continual envelopment by the new air. The sun is not usually any help with advection fog, since this sort of situation often betokens plenty of cloud at higher levels.

Even without the extreme of a frozen land to cool on, the passage of air over progressively colder latitudes, say from the Azores to the British Isles, can give quite enough cooling to produce fog or stratus. There is no easy clearance to this while over the sea, since sea surface temperature changes so little day by day. Clearance must await a change of wind bringing drier air. Sea fog which drifts off the sea on to land may clear after quite a short journey across heating land.

SEA-FOG TACTICS

For yachtsmen, sea fog holds the same perils as afflict motorists in land fog: inability to see and be seen. The comparatively low speeds at which boats move is of little consequence if several thousand tons of motorised shipping at even a few knots come up against a small sailing yacht becalmed and with no manoeuvrability. Sea fog also can be very patchy because the surface temperature fluctuates with the continual upwellings and sinkings of water. A general risk of fog at sea can be fairly accurately predicted if the dew point of air is near the average temperature of the surface of the water, but the detailed location of patches cannot be determined.

Sea fog can form quite suddenly. I once sat on a sunny beach with other parents watching children racing in sailing boats when suddenly the whole fleet disappeared alarmingly in fog. By luck the boats were close together at the time, and by judgement they kept close together, remembered the drift of wind was on to shore, set their sails to run before it and inevitably ran aground on the beach again and into sunshine. In dead calm or in a traffic lane it would not have been so easy.

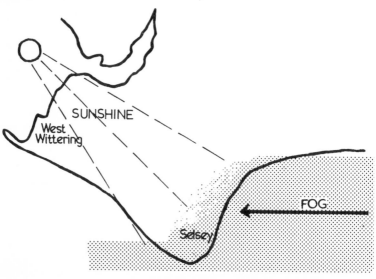

Evade sea fog by making a short journey downwind and inland

Sunshine and sea fog can be very close neighbours

Sea fog can occur at all times of the year but it tends to be most frequent in early spring when sea is at its minimum temperature. Even in summer a slight change in wind off the sea to bring air with a dew point near the temperature of the sea surface can cause fog to drift on shore. This can put a damper upon holiday proceedings but does not necessarily mean that you have to cancel picnic and bathing plans, merely that you should choose another place.

The direction to look is downwind and inland, and probably only a mile or two is necessary. The short journey air has to make over heating land will dissipate the fog entirely. It is hard to believe sometimes that such contrasting weathers can exist so close together, but they can, and there is quite a thrill in beating the weather at its own game and making an escape in the right direction. During an August heatwave, suddenly one morning an east wind with a long track down the English Channel wrapped Selsey in Hampshire in total chilly fog. Those of us who journeyed the few miles across the peninsula to West Wittering were rewarded with blazing sunshine all day and returned to find fog still enveloping Selsey (p 66).

I remember an even more dramatic contrast over a shorter distance. Wrapped in mackintoshes and headscarves my family walked from thick fog at one end of a half-mile promenade and at the other end came to a corner of beach dotted with sunbathers. Quite a small headland was serving as protection against the sea fog which was drifting on to shore at an acute angle (p 67).

CHAPTER NINE

COOLING BY LIFT — CONVECTION CLOUD

PRECIPITATION

Condensation in an air layer as a result of contact with colder surfaces gives water drops of such small size that they remain suspended in air as fog, or shallow low cloud. It requires considerably more cooling, such as is provided by a mechanical lift, before condensation can fall to the ground as rain, sleet, snow or hail. This occurs from thick clouds, which consist of three basic condensation forms. There are water drops at temperatures above 0°C; there are supercooled drops at temperatures below 0°C; and there are ice crystals. The lower the temperature, the greater the proportion of ice crystals to supercooled drops; the tops of very high clouds are entirely of ice.

Within a thick cloud these condensation forms move about and come into collision with each other. Small water drops coalesce to form larger drops, ice crystals cling together to form snow-flakes, and supercooled drops freeze on contact with ice crystals. Eventually such combinations become weighty enough to fall out of the cloud. Some of this precipitation may evaporate again before reaching ground. The rest falls as rain if temperatures are high enough to melt ice crystals. In winter, when freezing level is near the ground, and over mountains where the extra height gives lower temperatures, precipitation may reach the ground as snow. Hail is the result of large drops being tossed up and down in vertical currents within a cloud, alternately collecting additional water and then freezing, till ice stones acquire sufficient weight to overcome upthrusting air currents and fall to ground. Because of their large and solid nature they take much longer to thaw than snowflakes and consequently can reach ground level still frozen even in summer.

This is only a brief summary of a precipitation process which is still a subject of study for research meteorologists, to whom we can leave the unravelling of theoretical complexities. The end products are only too familiar to everyone, and it is more important for the layman to understand why the thick clouds form, so that he has some idea of the weather they bring.

COOLING BY THERMAL LIFTING

Cooling sufficient to produce thick clouds capable of precipitating results when air is lifted into regions of lower atmospheric pressure, with the consequent exaction of temperature tax (see p 28). The most powerful lifting mechanism is initiated by the heat of the sun and leads to the formation of convection clouds. To talk of 'cooling . . . by the heat of the sun' sounds like double dutch, but I deliberately use the words in juxtaposition.

The development of convection cloud is a two-tier operation. *First*, the sun heats the land and, by successive warming of shallow layers of air in contact, creates a buoyancy situation which causes thermal up-currents to develop (p 21). Down-currents follow as a necessary consequence, to fill the voids left by up-currents. *Secondly*, air which rises in the up-currents is subjected to the temperature taxation imposed with decreasing pressure. It cools as it rises. This is a quite separate development in the air's history, and has nothing to do with the fact that the sun is shining except insofar as sunshine keeps the mechanical current in existence.

When the sun sets, thermals die out and that is the beginning of the end of surface air's journey upwards.

Air rising in a thermal will cool at first at approximately 3°C per 1000ft. Sooner or later, depending upon its vapour content, dew point will be reached and condensation will occur; this forms cloud base. Provided that the thermal is still pushing upwards, air will continue to cool, at a somewhat reduced rate, building up a thickness of cloud. The depth of cloud which results depends upon the buoyancy conditions of the day, not only at surface level where the thermal originates, but at all heights above the ground. Air can only continue to rise when its temperature is warmer than that of the air which surrounds it.

STABILITY AND INSTABILITY

On any day, the atmosphere has a particular temperature profile determined by its past history (p 27). If its rate of temperature fall

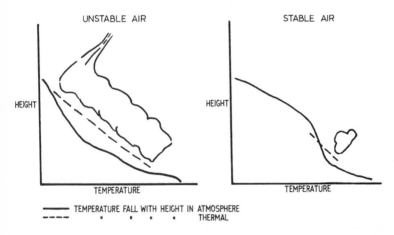

UNSTABLE AIR   STABLE AIR

HEIGHT   HEIGHT

TEMPERATURE   TEMPERATURE

————— TEMPERATURE FALL WITH HEIGHT IN ATMOSPHERE
------   "   "   "   "   THERMAL

Unstable air: temperature of the atmosphere falls more rapidly with height than temperature in the rising thermal; cloud can soar to great heights. Stable air: temperature of the atmosphere falls less rapidly with height than it does in the thermal, and only small clouds develop

71

with height is large, greater than the rate of temperature decrease which is being imposed upon the air in the thermal, then air can soar to great heights before losing buoyancy. Such an atmosphere is said to be *unstable*, because an initial movement at surface level escalates without restriction. If, however, the rate of temperature fall with height is small, then air rising in a thermal and cooling at the full standard rate will soon become colder than its surroundings and lose buoyancy. Such a situation is said to be *stable*, because the initial displacement of air gets no chance to continue upwards for long. If cloud develops at all it will be shallow, and if the air is very dry or the lid of surrounding warmer air is low, then no cloud will develop at all. On any particular day the atmosphere may be stable at some levels and unstable at others.

This can be illustrated pictorially with simple graphs. If temperature of the atmosphere falls rapidly with height, the graph showing this will be flatter than that showing the temperature of the rising air in the cloud. Up to great heights, the rising air will be warmer than its surroundings and therefore buoyant, and huge clouds will build up.

A slow temperature fall with height in the atmosphere shows a steeper gradient than the graph for the rising air. Where the two cross is the limit of convection, for if rising air cools any more its temperature will fall below that of the surrounding atmosphere, that is, it will become colder and non-buoyant.

In general, a northerly air stream, moving southwards and therefore warming in its lower level, will have a large temperature range with height and be unstable. A southerly air stream, moving northwards and therefore cooling in its lower level, will have a relatively small temperature range through its height and be stable. These characteristics are accentuated or diminished by different pressure patterns which will be discussed later.

CUMULUS CLOUDS

Clouds caused by convection in thermal currents are called

72

cumulus, from the way they pile up and accumulate. More homely descriptions—such as cotton-wool tufts, ice-cream portions, cauliflower heads, towering palaces—are plentiful, appealing according to interests or taste. They are certainly our most dramatic clouds.

Cumulus are relatively small in base area, the up-currents in which they develop being balanced by replacing down-currents in which there is no cloud. Unless it is a day of great instability, each cloud stands separate from the next, framed in a blue sky and with much of its vertical section visible. The colour range is wide, from brilliant white where the sunlight strikes it, to dark grey where hidden from the sun. Sometimes they drift in lines, called streets, downwind from a particular thermal source.

Since cumulus have no existence apart from the up-currents, they are diurnal clouds when over land, forming in the morning and dispersing again at night. While building up they have sharp thrusting contours which change as one watches; when on the decline their contours are blurred. The height of cloud base varies according to the humidity of the atmosphere and the extent of surface heating. Dew point may be reached around 1,000ft if air is moist, and bases may be considerably uneven at first because of variations in moisture at ground level and the different rates at which ground surfaces heat. But once thermals are strong enough to mix the lower levels of air uniformly, the bases of small cumulus often appear as even as if sliced off with a knife.

Cumulus have two wind systems to obey. They travel on the horizontal pressure wind of the day, and they also have their own built-in vertical winds, which are the cause of their very existence. To people below, the result is considerable gustiness. The up-draughts at leading edges and down-draughts at rear edges of quite small cumulus cause fluctuations of wind speed and direction at surface level which are noticeable enough to be utilised with effect by yachtsmen sailing on open water. On rivers or small inland lakes, cloud gusts get inextricably muddled with other gusts and variations caused by surface obstructions.

CUMULONIMBUS

When conditions are suitable for large cumulus development, the individual clouds become harder to see, each partly obscuring the next. On a very unstable day, clouds jostle together so closely that they present an almost continuous cloud cover for people beneath. Only occasional patches of blue sky can be seen, but colour gradation is still fairly marked. Black and grey contours are seen against fleeting glimpses of intense white tops which are catching the sunlight. These tops may be over 7 miles high and are entirely composed of ice crystals. At the upper limit of convection this ice cloud may spread outwards under the lid of warmer air above, giving a characteristic anvil top. Ice takes longer to dissipate than water, and residual ice cloud may trail on the upper wind long after the lower part of the cloud has dissolved.

Light showers can fall from quite modest-sized 'cauliflower' clouds. In the huge 'towers', drops can get carried up and down several times before being released, and the resulting shower can be very heavy. A cumulus which is able to produce a shower is called a cumulonimbus, or, more familiarly, a cunimb. A cunimb with anvil top can be assumed to be on the decline, often to be replaced by an adjacent active cloud with hard billowing contours.

Underneath cunimb, the up-draughts into the base of the cloud are like the suction of a giant vacuum cleaner, and are often strong enough to counteract the normal surface wind in the immediate vicinity. Though the cloud continues to advance on the upper wind (at about 10,000ft), at ground level the cloud *appears* to be going the other way because of the suction. Do not be misled into thinking a miracle is suddenly blowing such a cloud away from you. It may be advancing ruthlessly, and surface wind will return to normal once the cloud has passed. Immediately under the cloud conditions can be very wild, the up-currents at the leading edge being followed by a cold down-draught and rain from the centre of the cunimb. If at sea, reefing and battening down is a wise precaution in advance of their arrival. Inland,

74

where a cluttered horizon often prevents much advance warning, be prepared for any eventuality in wind direction and strength for a few moments.

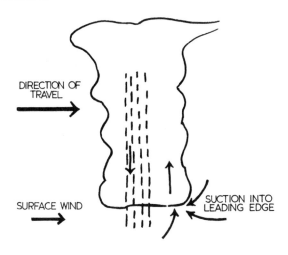

Suction into the leading edge of a large cunimb causes considerable fluctuation of wind speed and direction

THUNDERSTORMS

King of all cunimb are the thunderstorms. In very large clouds with strong up-currents water drops may split up and ice crystals splinter before being able to fall to ground against the thermal thrust. The process is thought to be contributory to the build-up of separate electric charges within the cloud, and when the air is no longer able to act as insulator between the positive and negative charges, lightning occurs. Thunder is the noise produced as the air suddenly expands by the heat of the flash. The exact reasons for thunderstorms are complex and much has still to be learnt. To investigate the actual structure of cunimb, the United States army co-operated with the US Weather Bureau in a fact-finding programme after the last war. Five planes were flown simultaneously through cunimb at staggered heights with instructions to keep hands off controls, once these had been levelled and adjusted for safe speeds, so that the up- and down-currents did the rest. It was found in the course of a series of such flights that some tops of clouds reached 60,000ft, that temperatures at cloud tops were sometimes as low as $-50°C$; and that up-draughts were occasionally as strong as 5,000ft per minute. The exercise needed as much nerve as any of the hazards of war!

There are two main types of thunderstorm. There are those that form in an atmosphere which is unstable from the ground upwards and are triggered off by daily heating over land. These are most likely to occur in the afternoon, dying out at night, and are most frequent in early spring when air of northerly origin may be very cold, but land temperatures rise rapidly under a sun of fairly high elevation.

There are also thunderstorms that form in an unstable layer of air which exists above a very stable surface layer of air. Because of the stability of the lower air, little or no cumulus develops during a normal day, and in summer the situation leads to our all too rare heatwaves. After successive days of such sunshine, the temperature of air in the lower levels builds up enough to break through the inversion and then cumulus develop rapidly in the air above. This happens in late afternoon or early evening, and if the upper air is very unstable then the down-currents from one cloud are enough to force adjacent air upwards and trigger off the next storm. This becomes a self-perpetuating see-saw in the upper air and independent of the fact that the sun may have set. Though each particular storm cloud may not have a life of more than an hour, the continual formation of new cells gives the impression that one storm lasts a whole night. Such storms are sometimes mere interludes in a continuing heatwave, or they can herald its decay, with another weather system gaining precedence.

These high-level cunimb have a rather different appearance from those which form in air which is unstable from the ground upwards. For one thing they are usually extremely hard to see in the distance, because the lower stable air has collected smoke and dirt underneath the temperature inversion for several days. Most heatwave skies appear whitish for this reason, and downwind from an industrial area can be yellow or dark grey. Not till advancing clouds are almost overhead, so that they can be seen through a minimum thickness of such haze, can they be discerned as weird sprouting turrets, which have earned the name of castellanus. The spindly vertical growth emphasises the sudden release of frustrated energy.

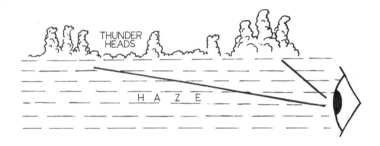

High-level thunderclouds look like weird turrets, hard to see till nearly overhead because there is often considerable haze at lower levels

CUMULUS OVER THE SEA

Though the majority of cumulus clouds originate over land because that is where the strongest thermals are found, they can form over the sea if sea surface temperature is warmer than the air passing over it. A northerly air stream moving south over the sea comes into this category, mainly in winter and spring; also a cold easterly air stream from the continent in winter, moving across the North Sea. Because of the extra moisture supply, cloud base is often lower than it would be over land. Moreover, since the sea surface temperature only changes imperceptibly over a short period of time, cumulus which form over the sea do not disperse at night as they do over land. Consequently, if wind is off-sea, coastal areas may continue to have cumulus or showers during the night, while none occur inland.

EFFICIENCY OF SHOWERS

As a means of converting water vapour back into liquid state for the benefit of our economy, the shower cloud is not a very efficient mechanism. If the shower is light, it remains on the surface of soil and evaporates again soon after the cloud has passed. If the shower is heavy, far too high a proportion goes to waste before it has time to penetrate. Catchment areas such as rivers and reservoirs will fill generously but the capacity of smaller channels like ditches and streams may be overtaxed by run-off from the surface. Roads flood, basements fill, and the water level in underground drainage systems rises rapidly, to the danger of anyone working below. The trouble is accentuated if a previous drought has left a hard impenetrable crust to the ground. In June 1967 a tragic accident occurred to a caving party at Mossdale in Yorkshire. A long period of dry weather was broken by a sudden storm which drained by every surface channel possible into the caves and waterways, drowning six people before they could get to safety. The accident could equally well have occurred had the ground been waterlogged, but then the already swollen state of underground channels would have been warning enough. Probably the most suitable state of soil for receiving such storm water is a surface layer already wet and receptive for more and a subsoil still dry enough to absorb.

In urban areas the flooding problem is accentuated by the increasing acreage of concrete from which surface water channels rapidly via drains into the rivers. Sailing boats which are dependent upon wind alone as motive power are supersensitive to any increase in the strength of river stream. Before the last war one could usually reckon on a time lapse of something like 24 hours before heavy rain percolated through the soil and made the stream too fast to combat. Recently, rapid drainage from new housing sites upstream can cause response of stream within very few hours.

In a domestic garden, the danger of a heavy shower is that the sheer drenching effect of being caught out in the downpour may lull one into thinking that garden thirst has been adequately quenched. The shower may have done nothing more than moisten the surface and serve only to aggravate any preceding drought situation. The tempting water near the surface can cause roots to strike upwards to find it, leaving them more vulnerable than ever to evaporating airs.

In the garden, light but persistent watering is the most effective. Artificially it can be achieved by hosing; in weather it is achieved by the flat sheet cloud which we shall discuss in the next chapter.

READING CUMULUS CLOUDS

A professional forecaster's duty is to anticipate the formation and size of cumulus before these even start developing; and he has plenty of technical information to help him. Without the same aids, the amateur can at any rate watch the clouds once they start to form and anticipate the next stage of their development. This can enable him to predict weather with reasonable accuracy for a few hours ahead, and also give valuable information about wind and locality. The skies shown on the following pages, 80-4, are used as examples.

1. The sky over the sea is cloudless, so the line of cumulus ahead must mean some extra thermal source. (I can tell you that it is the French coast because I happen to know; but remember that the above titbit of reasoning could stand you in good stead if you were ever unfortunate enough to be shipwrecked. A small patch of cumulus in an otherwise clear sky is a far better signpost to the nearest desert island than any wheeling albatross!)

The cumulus are not very large but have upthrusting tops. If the time is early or mid-morning, and they continue to grow thus, they could well produce showers by late afternoon. If the time is already noon, then they have not made much progress for so many hours of sunshine and probably will not give showers but disperse by late afternoon.

Clear visibility indicates reasonable instability, though this may be partly due to lack of dirt sources over the sea.

We are not close enough to shore to see if the clouds follow the coastline exactly, but this is highly probable. The tops are crisply outlined, suggesting they are still over the thermal source. Wind over France is therefore probably along or on to the shore. If it had been off-shore, the nearest cumulus tops would be blurred as they drifted on to the sea and away from the thermal source.

2. The south English coast has receded out of sight, but is sign-posted by a procession of cunimb marching along the coast. The clouds under the anvil tops are on the wane, but the billowing contours behind indicate still-developing clouds. South-coast inhabitants are frequently taking shelter from heavy showers, and the considerable lower cloud hiding the bases of the giants indicates few breaks when there might be sunshine.

Both size of clouds and sharp visibility indicate very unstable air. If the time is late afternoon, showers will ease off in a few hours; if the time is before noon, frequent showers will continue for several more hours.

Wind over England is almost parallel to the shore (left to right) as indicated by the trail of ice cloud in the anvil tops, and by the fact that there is no intervening cloud between boat and shore. Huge clouds such as this would not disperse quickly enough to give such clear skies if they were drifting off land.

3. Here we look at cumulus more nearly overhead. This bustling Solent scene is taken below clouds not much bigger than those in p 80. The Hampshire coast is on the right, the Isle of Wight on the left. The time is summer and therefore the sea is cooler than the land.

The clouds which cover the sea must have formed over land and drifted on a wind off Hampshire—the sheer quantity implies formation over the mainland rather than over the small area of the Isle of Wight.

Yachtsmen, who find the above statement self-evident because they can see the way the sails are set, should note the further implication that on this occasion the pressure wind was strong enough to overcome any tendency for a sea breeze to blow *on* to shore. On this day, therefore, approximately the same wind is blowing on either side of the Solent, possibly a bit stronger on the Isle of Wight side since the pressure wind might be increased by a sea breeze effect blowing on to the Isle coast.

Concerning the future development of these clouds, if the time is early morning showers could well occur in afternoon; if the time is afternoon they have probably reached their limit.

4. In built-up areas it is rare to see the whole depth of a large cumulus because of lack of open horizon. A firm 'cauliflower head' such as this should be enough to warn of showers.

To find out if this particular one is coming one's way, watch it for a few minutes against a fixed object such as a roof top or tree trunk. Whether or not this one is en route for an observer, remember that the presence of one such cloud top like this indicates that others are developing too. They will be dotted at random over the sky, some areas may escape without any, others have more than their fair share.

Showers will not last long but can be heavy, and they often have a very well-defined beginning and end. If the edge only of a cloud like this passes overhead it may water the back garden but not the front, wet the pavement one side of the road but not the other.

The usual cumulus timetable applies. If you are watching this sky during the morning you can expect showers to persist during the afternoon. If the time is afternoon, showers will not continue much longer, unless they happen to be drifting off the sea on to a coastal area.

5. This is a thoroughly lazy sky. Lack of any high cloud to mask the sun and the firm flat bases of many of the cumulus indicate that thermals are still rising. The shallow depth of the clouds indicates very stable conditions with warmer surroundings reached soon after cloud base is formed. Cloud base is high, indicating dry air.

If the hour is already afternoon, the clouds will disperse very soon. If the hour is before noon and something happens to increase the stability of the air still further then the clouds will disperse well before the normal evening time. The very blurred and flat tops indicate that this is happening. Give frequent glances at the clouds within the next half hour and you will probably find that they are disappearing altogether, a sure sign heralding settled fine weather in summer.

Note the lack of sharp colour contrast between clouds and sky, which is whitish in the distance because of the thickness of haze through which one is looking. Overhead it is rather more blue, though nothing like the bright blue of an unstable atmosphere.

CHAPTER TEN

COOLING BY LIFT — FRONTAL CLOUD

Flat sheet cloud results when huge masses of air come together from separate directions and therefore have different temperature, humidity and density characteristics. They cannot blend together immediately, any more than can two liquids of different density, like syrup and water. Mixing takes time. In the meantime, they seek a solution to the dilemma of density difference by rising one above the other. The boundary between such air masses is called a front, in the battlefield sense. The colder heavier air is the aggressor, the warm lighter air the victim forced to escape upwards.

WARM FRONTS

A warm front exists when warm air is pushed up against cooler air and must slither upwards in order to continue its progress. In vertical cross-section, the boundary takes the form of a gradual slope and the lifting is slow but persistent. As the air lifts into regions of lower pressure it cools, condenses and forms flat sheet cloud, from which rain falls once cloud has thickened to about 8000ft from the ground. Cloud continues to lower towards the boundary at ground level, known as the surface front, and in the

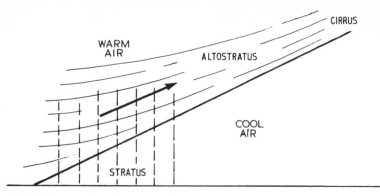

Vertical section through a warm front

wet air below the front turbulence results in fragmentary patches of stratus which often appear to be scudding past at very high speed. It may well be moving fast, but in part this is illusion due to its very low height above ground, perhaps 200-300ft, and often covering hill tops and mountains.

Warm fronts usually have a forward velocity of their own, so that to an observer on the ground the effect is of a gradual increase and thickening of cloud all over the sky. Let us look at two stages in the development of such a sky (pp 87, 88).

The first sign of approaching trouble is often less noticeable as cloud than as a slight lessening of heat from the sun. One feels a chill, looks upwards and finds one can almost bear to look right at the sun. Then it becomes apparent that overhead are wisps of feathery ice-crystal cloud called cirrus, often sharply drawn and trailing down and backwards as they get caught up in different wind speeds at various levels. Towards the horizon the wisps gradually merge into a complete white veil.

The cumulus which have previously formed in thermals decrease in depth and disperse as the veil cuts off the heat of the sun (p 87).

The message is unmistakeable. Rain is on the way within a few hours. It is a day for carrying mackintoshes, for burning dry garden rubbish before it gets wet, for bedding out garden plants rather than wasting time with the hoe. Give frequent glances at the sky to gauge the speed of advance of the upper cloud and the arrival of rain. If instead of thickening further the cloud breaks up, the front is losing momentum and rain will not occur.

As the veil thickens to solid grey cloud known as altostratus, the sun gradually disappears altogether (p 88). After a sky like this, usually within the hour, rain can be expected. It will be light at first, and may either remain light or become heavy but is characteristically continuous. Its duration will vary according to the activity of the front but can be counted in hours rather than minutes. Rain is widespread because the sheet cloud may cover whole counties or countries.

When the surface front arrives, there may be a burst of rather heavier rain, and this is a hopeful sign for imminent clearance. Cloud will break, rain cease and there may be a noticeable rise in temperature as the warm air engulfs the observer.

Small cumulus flatten, upper sheet cloud increases, rain in a few hours

Sun almost obscured by formless grey cloud, altostratus, rain within the hour (*see p 87*)

COLD FRONTS

A cold front exists when cold air pursues warm air, undercutting impatiently so that warm air escapes not just by a gentle slither upwards but with a violent upthrust sufficient to induce cunimb and heavy showers, often with thunder. Because the upthrust is delivered along a boundary between the two airs, the cunimb form a well-marked line in contrast to the well-spaced clouds forming in thermals.

The observer will get much shorter warning of the approach of a cold front than he gets for a warm front. The photograph on p 90 shows huge banks of angry clouds which are advancing on the wind to deliver a downpour.

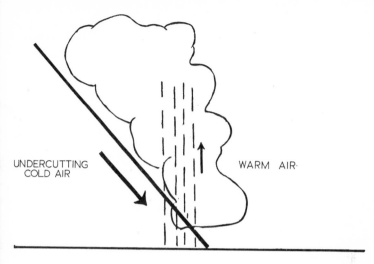

Vertical section through a cold front

When the cold front passes, the deluge stops with dramatic suddenness, having delivered in a few minutes as much or more water than in the several hours' duration of a warm front. The line of clouds rolls aside, revealing a brilliant blue sky in which individual cumulus may develop (p91). The temperature becomes noticeably colder.

Though psychologically cheering, the transformation is not without its troubles, particularly to the motorist. Glistening roads, wet and dirty windscreens, possibly even a low altitude sun, make visibility extremely difficult. It becomes essential to stop and clean windows, and dark glasses may be temporarily necessary till roads dry. This they do fairly quickly, because air behind a cold front is usually dry and often windy.

For a bird's-eye view of the clouds shown on pp 87-91, turn back to the satellite photograph on p 13. Note how the sheet cloud ahead of the warm front contrasts with the individual cumulus behind the well-marked cold front.

Cold front downpour imminent (see p 88)

FRONTAL DEPRESSIONS

There is a favourite meeting place in mid-Atlantic for cold polar air and warm subtropical air, and from here are generated the depressions and changeable weather typical of the British Isles. The initial confrontation of airs develops a wave motion at the tip of which pressure falls. The wave grows into an active depression, with a sector of warm air caught in the pincer movement of harrying cold front behind and obstinate cool air ahead. Seen in plan on a weather chart, the warm front followed by cold front are drawn as lines with semi-circular blobs or sharp points, and the whole system travels at varying speeds and usually towards the east or north-east. One frontal depression often breeds others, which follow in a kind of family sequence.

Fronts and depressions have a birth, lifetime and death; and

Cold front disappears into distance after giving torrential downpour (see p 89)

according to the stage at which they are encountered, so does the weather intensity vary. There are the young and the old, the weak and the forceful, those that die a peaceful death and those that get a rejuvenating injection of contrasting airs to start life all over again. The important thing to remember is that no depression moves from A to B unchanged. It is always being

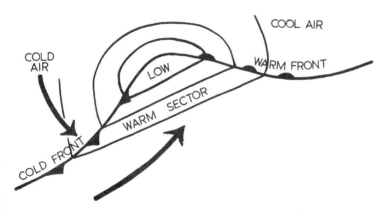

The front between two air masses often develops a wave motion and low-pressure circulation

91

modified by intake of other airs from the periphery of its circulation, just as the character of a human being continually develops according to the situations he meets.

In a young depression destined to make its mark in life, pressure falls rapidly, more so nearer the centre than further away. Since this involves a tightening of the pressure gradient, wind speeds increase and add to the unpleasantness of the weather.

A favourite track for Atlantic depressions is towards Iceland, which receives more than its fair share of strong winds and foul weather. Being nearer these centres, Scotland suffers more than the rest of the British Isles. Once past their prime and with the energy of the fronts dispersed by mixing of airs, such depressions often spend a leisurely retirement over Scandinavia before losing their separate identity.

In the regions of the world where there is an ample supply of moisture from very warm seas, such low pressure systems can develop into the strength of hurricanes, which means an *average* wind speed over 70mph. The damage they cause to life and property is enormous. However, once under way they pursue a purposeful path which can be fairly accurately predicted and it has been possible to develop with considerable success an extensive warning system in hurricane areas. Though hurricanes are not generally part of the British weather scene, the deeper depressions can well bring gusts of hurricane force. A depression crossing Scotland on the night of 14/15 January 1968 gave one recorded gust of 126mph. Much damage was done, Glasgow in particular suffering extensively.

Less easy to forecast is the behaviour of fronts which seem to weary before reaching the British coast. Cloud breaks, the odd spots of rain peter out, and then, as one is about to dismiss them as finished, they get a wicked renewal of life, causing far more trouble than they ever did to begin with. They often have their genesis in the British south-west approaches and then the problem of forecasting is aggravated because of the paucity of weather-reporting stations in such a large sea area.

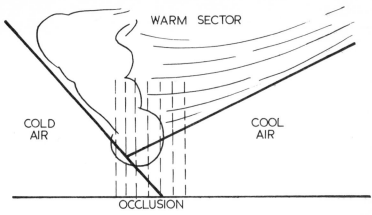

WARM SECTOR

COLD
AIR

COOL
AIR

OCCLUSION

When a cold front overtakes a warm front and lifts the warm sector off the ground, the surface boundary is called an occlusion

OCCLUSIONS

Cold fronts usually travel faster than warm fronts because of their aggressive activity, and therefore at some stage of associated travel in a depression, the cold front catches up with the warm. In cross-section this means that the warm air is lifted right off the ground, so that an observer misses out the warm-sector stage, passing through one violent clearance only. This is known as an occlusion or occluded front. Since dying fronts are usually occluded, it is the re-birth of occlusions which often give the nastiest surprises.

TIMING OF DEPRESSIONS AND FRONTS

There is nothing diurnal about frontal cloud as there is with convection cloud. Fronts and depressions come at any time of day or night, but occasionally a periodicity evolves among systems travelling in quick succession. I have known ideal weather, when for weeks, it seemed, there was frontal rain at night and sunshine by day, perfect for garden growth. There have also been dreadful spells when frontal belts have occurred day after day, with skies clearing tantalisingly in the evenings to remind one of the benefit a clear sky could have given by day. Such spells can be particularly disastrous in late summer by preventing the ripening of crops and fruit and encouraging the diseases which thrive in moist warm conditions.

The old saying, 'Rain before seven, fine before eleven', dies hard and is as good a rule as any for gauging the duration of warm-front rain if no forecast or weather map is to hand. Four hours is an average sort of duration. The hours of seven and eleven have no special significance, but they conveniently rhyme and cunningly extend the range of the prediction. Most people assume the dictum to refer to morning, and seven o'clock is a normal time for getting up and taking a first look at the weather. So the prediction covers not only rain which has just started and might have a total duration of only four hours, but also that which has been falling unobserved during the hours of sleep. Obviously, the longer rain has already been falling, the greater the chance of clearing before a further four hours has passed.

WARM-SECTOR WEATHER

Actually in the warm sector, weather follows the diurnal pattern of cumulus formation by day and clear skies at dusk. Since the warm-sector air is usually stable, only small clouds develop and weather is fine and sunny during the warmer months of the year. However, since the warm-sector air is often very moist if it has come directly from the Atlantic, cooling at night frequently causes fog or low stratus, and in the colder months this may not always clear next day.

SNOW BELTS

The terms 'warm' and 'cold' used in connection with fronts are relative terms only. A confrontation between warm and hot summer airs is as likely to cause frontal weather as confrontation between cool and cold, or cold and bitter. When cold and bitter cold meet, fronts give snow instead of rain. Over continents in high latitudes rapidly cooling land is consistently reflected by very low air temperatures, and snow is more usual than rain. Within these snow regions, there are again vast differences in degree of cold. The temperatures experienced in some parts of Siberia or America are beyond the imagination even of those experiencing the very cold winter of western Europe. At the other extreme the people of Great Britain, surrounded by relatively warm sea, feel badly treated when temperatures fall even as far as 0°C.

There is only a marginal difference between snow and rain, and because the lowest British temperatures are never far from the critical melting level of snow it is often very difficult to forecast whether a frontal belt will give snow or rain in the British Isles. Even if snow does fall, it is likely to be 'wet' snow, liable to melt easily with slight local rises in temperature. Moreover, any pressure on snow lowers its melting point slightly. This has little consequence if temperatures are far below 0°C; snow then remains 'dry' and spectacular machines can suck it up and blow it off to one side to keep roadways clear. With wet snow, processing through a machine may well result in enough melting to make snow a slushy mess, clogging the machine. The same sort of thing happens on the actual surface of the road. If snow is wet, the passage of traffic will melt it in the centre thoroughfare (p 96), while the slush may be unable to escape down blocked drains at the side. The wet centre surface may then re-freeze as ice if temperature falls at night, giving a surface like a skating rink. It is doubly dangerous because not visible, and for this reason is often known as black ice. With much colder air on the continents, pressure of traffic compacts the snow without melting it and grit and ashes laid on top become embedded and make a reasonable motoring surface. It is important to bear in mind these differences in quality of snow when grumbling about the failure of local authorities to keep traffic moving.

Wet snow melts under the pressure of traffic during the day, and re-freezes to ice with the additional cooling at night

COLORATION OF SKIES

There is a much quoted weather tag which states, with local variation in detail:

Red sky at night, shepherd's delight;
Red sky in morning, shepherd's warning.

It contains a germ of truth, and refers to the coloration of the underside of high cloud by a low sun. Most frontal belts approach the British Isles from the west so that a rising sun in the east will light up the cloud base overhead or advancing from the west. Such belts clear away to the east, so that a low setting sun will colour the retreating cloud. The trouble is that not all cloud is frontal, and colours vary considerably according to the amount of dust and moisture in the atmosphere. I personally have found the tag a broken reed, and prefer to enjoy coloured skies for their artistic merit only.

The coloration in cloud through which the moon can be seen is a more reliable guide. When light passes through cloud of well-formed ice crystal, it is refracted as if passing through glass prisms, and results in an optical phenomenon called a halo. This is a thin ring of light of wide diameter, whitish in colour but with a reddish tinge on the *inside*, and sometimes embellished by extra arcs in geometric pattern. So, when 'the moon in haloes hides her head . . .' there is high ice-crystal cloud and warm front rain is on the way.

A halo must not be confused with a corona which is seen around a moon viewed through a thin cloud of water drops, perhaps stratus or dispersing patches of convection cloud. A corona has blue colour on the inside, red on the *outside*, and there may be several concentric rings at a time. It has no particular significance as a sign of rain; it merely helps the observation of cloud.

Another good coloration sign is the abnormally enlarged and red appearance of the setting sun when low in the horizon. This is caused by distortion of vision and scattering of blue light when viewed through moist surface air. Since one can only see the setting sun if there is no cloud to obscure it, the probability is that over land there will be radiation cooling at night, leading to fog.

CHAPTER ELEVEN

INTENSIFICATION AND DIMINUTION OF CLOUD

LIFT OVER HIGH GROUND

There is one simple lifting mechanism which produces cloud on its own, or accentuates cloud and rain which already exist. This is the necessary lift air must make to surmount obstacles which bar its progress. On an otherwise clear day, lift over hills may be enough to produce stratus cloud over their tops (p 99). Cloud appears to be stationary all day but in reality is an ever-changing mass of water drops which form on the windward side as the air lifts, and disperse on the leeward side as the air sinks again. Sometimes the rise and fall of air over a mountain range is sufficiently marked to induce a repetitive wave motion for some distance downwind. Then small lenticular-shaped clouds will form at regular intervals on the crests of these waves.

If cumulus or frontal cloud fill the sky generally, then the extra lift over high ground can make light rain moderate, heavy showers torrential and low cloud even lower. The familiar phrase in forecasts, 'cloud covering high ground' (see p 100), should never be taken lightly. For cloud is only cloud to the observer if there is clear air between it and him and its base can be seen. When *inside* a cloud it warrants the name of fog.

Lift over high ground alone gives stratus when air is moist

Fog has its hazards for pedestrians as well as for fast-moving traffic. I am not thinking of the ordered paths of town or village where one can grope one's way around, however thick may be the fog, but of open expanses of high moor where fog baffles all sense of direction, or mountainsides where one false step on to a path which does not exist can prove fatal. In already foul weather, low cloud can probably be *seen* to cover high ground and there is little temptation to venture out. What is not obvious, but must be anticipated, is that frontal cloud only just starting to spread into an area may quell the fine day and may lower to obliterate all landmarks while a walking party is already far from base, possibly inexperienced and inadequately clad. It may sound ludicrous to think of the weather as dangerous in connection with mere walking, but every year there is some accident on this account. For good reason has the weather been considered the best barrier to escape from the prison on Dartmoor. Respect for the weather should be as much part of the planning for hike, pony trek or climbing expedition as it is for sports like flying or sailing; the expert in any sporting field will always acknowledge this. Watch the sky to see if there are any signs like those on pp 87–8 which could indicate rapid lowering of cloud, and if in any doubt consult a weather office.

It is not only the possibility of danger that should make one weather-conscious before setting off on an excursion into the heights. Consider the sheer frustration of spending money and time on, for instance, taking a mountain train to the summit to see a renowned and fabulous view to find that visibility is only a few yards! If in unfamiliar country, consult the local inhabitants on the weather peculiarities of their mountains. In your own locality, study the foibles of high-ground weather so that you instinctively adapt any general forecast to suit your particular terrain.

At night, under clear skies, lift over high ground may add to the normal troubles of radiation cooling, but only if there is the

Lift over high ground lowers frontal cloud to cover mountain tops

impetus of a pressure wind of about 10mph to force air upwards. With calm or lighter wind the down-slope katabatic effect (p 26) will be dominant and cooling air will drain into the valleys. Given the requisite wind speed, over heights of only a few hundred feet, a complete cloud cover can replace a starlight sky in a matter of moments. This is of dire consequence to pilots flying in hilly country, whether the cloud comes right down or whether a stronger wind keeps it a few hundred feet above ground.

As in the case of radiation fog, hill stratus and perfect night differ by only a hair's breadth. Conditions may be ripe for deterioration for an hour or so before anything happens, and for the observer watching there is an uncanny feeling of suspense as if being watched by an unseen enemy. There is an airfield, Little Rissington, which rises 750ft above sea level on the edge of the Cotswolds and is the first major obstacle for southwesterly winds, already moist from a long Atlantic track, coming up the Bristol Channel. The lift over the hill is the last straw and on susceptible nights that station is always the first in the area to be blanketed by stratus. These nights are not the kind one would choose for training pilots because of the risk of being unable to land. But during the war all possible flying time had to be utilised, and that included the clear southwesterly nights. Many a pilot practising 'circuits and bumps' was dismayed at suddenly seeing the runway lights below disappear as if turned off by switch. The saving grace for this particular airfield is that neighbouring lower stations often have enough time to receive diversions before they too have to close down. A slight difference in wind direction, WSW instead of SW, makes all the difference to this airfield. The longer land track to windward leaves surface air drier so that the cooling induced by lift over the hills may be insufficient to lower temperature to dew point.

LIFT BY CONVERGENT AIR

Lift over mountains produces local deteriorations of weather within an area covered by a particular pressure pattern. There is also a lifting mechanism which is caused by a low pressure pattern itself.

Wind blows round a centre of low pressure in an anticlockwise direction, with wind at ground level backed from that at 2000ft (p 34). The result is that more air flows in towards the centre at ground level than high above. The excess air which piles in below must be accommodated by a lift upwards of air above the centre. This is called convergence and is persistent enough on its own to render any depression a potential rain factory.

In the case of a travelling depression with associated fronts, convergence accentuates the bad weather caused by the meeting of air masses, but the misery is limited to the period the fronts take to pass by. In the case of a stationary depression whose associated fronts may no longer be clearly defined, convergence alone can cause rain for days on end. This was the case over the south of England between 14 and 16 September 1968. Continuous rain gave an amount of rainfall only to be expected about once in several hundred years. Parts of Kent, Surrey and Essex had between 6 and 8in, and there was disastrous flooding, particularly in East Molesey where many low-lying homes were ruined by muddy waters from the swollen river. Even in my own garden, on high ground well out of reach of any river, soakaway pits were full to capacity and all plants were swimming in a sheet of water. I had to siphon off by hosepipe to lower ground a 4in deep pool covering the whole terrace against the house wall. It was one of the occasions when gale winds might have been preferable to lack of wind, since they would have sent the depression on its way earlier.

Often a marked change in wind direction round a depression causes frontal belts to develop. You will see in the accompanying diagram that there is not only convergent air giving lift but the opposing directions of the wind are bringing together airs of different origin. (Remember that this sort of map is for one moment of time only. A parcel of air on the west side of the circulation does not arrive unchanged on the east side, like a ball in a roulette wheel. It is constantly changed by airs fed into the circulation from the periphery.) A line of heavy showers develops which is akin to a cold front and is called a trough (a descriptive allusion to the shape of the isobars). Troughs can form frequently and rapidly round a low-pressure centre and one must be prepared for them at short notice. Once formed they can be timed for progress, but not until a well-defined position is established.

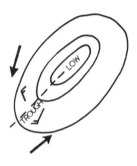

Convergence with rapidly changing isobar direction causes lines of showers called troughs, which are akin to cold fronts

DIMINUTION OF CLOUD

Fortunately, the depressing tale of cloud and rain caused by lifting mechanisms of one sort or another is ameliorated by some natural antidotes.

Time is the healer in the case of battles between air masses. Gradual mixing destroys boundary differences, cloud breaks into stratified patches and threatened rain fails to materialise.

Thermals over land cease when the sun sets and therefore cumulus clouds dissolve in the evening.

Obstacles like mountains remain firmly where they are, but fortunately have a leeward side. After the effort of rising to cross a barrier, air sinks thankfully on the other side into regions of higher pressure. This bestows a temperature bonus, air warms and thereby increases its thirst for water vapour, and cloud dissolves to meet the need. If the rise of air over the mountains in frontal weather is sufficient to increase noticeably the rainfall over the heights, then the sinking air on the far side will cause cloud base to become somewhat higher and rainfall lighter. Hence a barrier of high ground to windward affords considerable protection. In practical terms, as applied for instance to holidaymakers on the Welsh coast, it is useless to hope for relief from a wet day by going inland to the mountains, but the longer journey *beyond* the mountains could well be worth while. In climatological terms, conditions in the west of the British Isles, from which direction come most of the frontal belts, are too cloudy and wet to be suitable for commercial fruit farming. Inland, to leeward of the Welsh mountains, a better proportion of necessary rain and sunshine is obtained.

DIVERGENCE

Convergence in low-pressure circulations mercifully also has its antidote, in the high-pressure circulations called anticyclones. Wind round such centres blows in a clockwise direction, surface wind being as usual backed from wind direction at 2000ft above ground. This means that more air diverges from the centre at low level than higher up, necessitating a subsidence of air above the centre to replace the void. The subsiding air gets a temperature bonus as it sinks into regions of higher pressure (p 28) and consequently thermals from the ground reach warmer surroundings sooner. The tops of any cumulus start to dissolve and become diffuse-looking instead of crisp and billowing, though the bases may still be well defined by the thermals below. As subsidence continues the clouds get shallower and eventually disappear, which is what happened soon after the photograph on p 84 was taken. Dispersal of cloud by subsidence can occur at any time of day. Normal dispersal of cumulus in late afternoon, when thermals die out, usually results in blurred bases as well as blurred tops.

An anticyclone does not step in to take the place of a depression suddenly, but encroaches gradually via an intermediary stage called a 'ridge', which often gives the most perfect weather of all. There is enough subsidence to ensure that convection clouds remain small and picturesque, these interrupt the sun only intermittently so that air temperatures build up steadily but not oppressively, and there is usually a light wind—the centres of high pressure are often oppressively calm.

A ridge of high pressure often intervenes between consecutive depressions, giving brief respites of perhaps a day of decent weather between bouts of cloud and rain. The rise in pressure is considerable but of short duration, and often still low in the range of possible actual atmospheric pressures. All too soon pressure starts to fall again as the next depression approaches.

It is when cumulus clouds dissolve through subsidence, when no signs of spreading sheet cloud are visible and pressure continues to plod a steady upward path into the level of 1030mb and above, that the evidence heralds the advent of an anticyclone, with its absence of rain.

ANTICYCLONES

Whether one rejoices or despairs at the prospect of an anticyclone depends upon the season and length of day. In summer, clear skies and long hours of sunshine result in high temperatures which are only slightly relieved by brief periods of radiation cooling at night. Dew forms, and occasional mist or fog in low-lying moist areas, but all clear rapidly after sunrise. Temporary low cloud sometimes forms early in the morning when thermals start the development of cumulus clouds which almost immediately hit their heads on an upper layer of warm air. Clouds spread out into one flat sheet which breaks up again, as the sun gets higher, via an intermediary pancake shape before total dispersal (below). Providing pressure is still high and a heavy dew indicates that the night has been cloudless, then a formless grey sky early on a summer morning is nothing to worry about. It will be another hot sunny day.

A winter anticyclone is another matter. A short cloudless day is the forerunner of a long night giving more radiation cooling than a low-angle sun can counteract next day. The second night of cooling therefore starts with a lower air temperature than the first and possibly reaches frost level. The frost gets harder as clear nights continue, which is only likely when air is dry. In moist airs, and therefore a particular risk for island countries like Great Britain, cooling at night soon results in fog, which may persist for the duration of the anticyclone. It is for this reason that I cautiously specify the characteristic of anticyclonic weather as 'absence of rain'. The categorical statements 'dry' and 'fine' printed on the faces of many barometers are hardly appropriate when winter fog presses against the window.

Shallow cumulus spread over into a sheet of stratocumulus under an inversion, breaking up into pancake shapes and dispersing as the sun rises further

If there is a slight wind radiation fog may lift to low stratus, which still makes the weather far from 'fine' and has the well-earned title of 'anticyclonic gloom'. The dismal greyness of the cloud is often accentuated by smoke collected underneath a temperature inversion, and downwind of industrial areas acquires threatening khaki or black colours.

Anticyclones move but not quite in the same purposeful way as the travelling depressions. They nudge their way into position and once having gained the stage can be incredibly stubborn about leaving, perhaps persisting for weeks. They divert depressions on to different routes and then suddenly tire of their blocking tactics and slip away at short notice. Long-range forecasting in a well-established anticyclone is difficult for this reason.

OTHER CLOUD TYPES

The basic theme of cooling to dew point via contact with colder surfaces or via lift into regions of lower pressure, allows of many variations of cloud form according to topography and the temperature and humidity at different levels of the atmosphere. Smooth lenticular clouds, rolling billows, patterned mackerel skies, the contrail cloud forming in the wake of aircraft as they exude extra vapour into the air, are all examples which can be studied in cloud atlases. They often give helpful evidence to meteorologists about winds in the upper atmosphere, but do not easily aid the layman in his forecasting attempts. More important for the amateur is to understand thoroughly how wind at ground level behaves, and for this there are no visible clues like clouds.

CHAPTER TWELVE

THE BEHAVIOUR OF WIND

EVAPORATING POWER

In the ceaseless merry-go-round of water in our universe, air which is not already full to capacity with water vapour will drink from any sources it can find by the process of evaporation. The drier the air the more evaporation will take place. Also, the more air that passes over a source of moisture in a given time—in other words the stronger the wind—the more evaporation will take place.

Strong winds occur whenever there is a steep pressure gradient across the country—shown on a weather chart as closely packed isobars. These can be tightly spaced at any time of the year and orientated in any direction, allowing the possibility of gales from every point of the compass at all seasons. In the British Isles strong winds are most frequent in winter and usually from the Atlantic and therefore moist. But each summer has its quota of gales and each season its incidence of particularly dry winds.

In the garden appropriate action should be taken in advance. Tall herbaceous plants need staking, new climbing shoots must be tied in, and bean sticks planted firmly enough to withstand buffeting when they are covered in abundant foliage. In spring particularly, when young plants have not yet established their roots deep into the ground, watch for strong dry winds from Europe. They can be devastating in a garden, especially if accompanied by a stratus sheet on the edge of an anticyclone. A hot sun seems to remind the gardener that the soil is thirsty, probably because he feels thirsty too, and so the garden gets watered. But grey skies camouflage the equal evaporating power of a dry wind. This goes for winter time, too: by the end of a long spell with dry continental wind, dead twigs and leaves, under a hedge for instance, are like tinder and can catch alight with a few sparks from a nearby bonfire.

DISSIPATION OF HEAT

Warmth also is more easily dissipated by fast moving air, and temperatures of objects receiving heat from the sun do not rise nearly so fast in windy weather as in still. This can lead to a sense of false security about the temperatures that can build up *inside* a totally enclosed greenhouse or parked car. Outside in the wind there is no discomfort, but behind closed glass the penetrating sun may be building up uncomfortable or dangerous temperatures with no mitigating reduction by the wind. Open the windows to let the wind in a little.

GUSTINESS

Wind near the surface is never absolutely constant in speed because of turbulence caused by its surmounting or avoiding the many obstacles in its path. Variations from average speed are called gusts and lulls, and though these are most evident over land, they also occur in lesser degree over the sea.

The force that wind exerts is proportional to the square of its speed, so that if wind speed doubles, say from 5mph to 10mph in a gust, the force the wind exerts in that gust will quadruple (in the proportion of 25:100). Even at such relatively low speeds I have seen a gust capsize ignominiously an inattentive dinghy helmsman. At higher average velocities, which are already of uncomfortable strength, a gust of even slightly greater speed can have an alarming increase in the force it exerts.

In 1965, in a gale at Ferrybridge in the north of England, three out of eight cooling towers at a power station collapsed, and the others were all later found to have suffered structural damage. The gale was not exceptionally severe, blowing at an average speed of 40-50mph at the height of the storm; but there were gusts, timed over periods of three seconds, of around 80mph. The investigating committee concluded that it was the force of these sudden gusts which caused the trouble. The lesson learnt here was that in designing buildings allowance must be made not just for probable average wind speeds but for possible sudden gust strengths.

Gustiness can be a nuisance, as when umbrellas are blown inside out, or it can be a menace as when buffeting traffic on open roads. Cars with trailers, tall caravans or furniture vans, all of which present large surface areas to the force of the wind, are particularly susceptible to toppling if wind blows *across* the road they are travelling. Hence the new motorways, which cut straight through open country without benefit of protective hedges, often get special attention in weather forecasts.

All winds are gusty to a certain extent, but the worst are those where the horizontal factor is coupled with the up-and-down motion of convection weather. Large cumulus always cause particularly vicious gusts, while under the leading edges of shower clouds wind may go temporarily berserk.

FUNNELLING OF WIND

Despite occasional shows of strength, wind is basically lazy and always takes the easy route round an obstacle to avoid going over the top. It will bend itself round the end of a mountain range, giving a wind direction in that vicinity different from that indicated by the isobars, and it does the same round a corner of a house. Moreover if two houses, or rows of houses, are side by side with one easy gap between, this will be a favourite path for wind. Too much air will crowd through too small a gap and have to move faster to cope. Dustbin lids go flying and pedestrians get bowled over at the intersections of roads. Between mountain valley sides, the same sort of thing happens. A northerly wind funnelling down the constriction of the Rhône valley bursts out on the Mediterranean coast as the diabolical Mistral, filling holidaymakers' caravans with sand and capsizing yachts caught unawares at sea. One shouldn't be caught totally unawares of course. When the wind comes from that direction one should at least shut caravan and house windows, and delay unnecessary sailing, just in case.

On the roads, open bridges across steep-banked rivers become special hazards when wind is blowing along the line of the river. It is for this reason that bridges are sometimes temporarily closed during gales.

EDDIES

Wind not only swirls round corners of buildings or mountains, but also gets distorted by any surfaces it strikes. Some gets deflected on the windward side of the object, while air that pours over the top creates a lee eddy in the comparatively empty space on the other side. If you have difficulty in visualising such eddies, pause awhile when next you cross a bridge over fast-moving water and drop a small stick behind the bridge pillar on the downstream side. It will probably get held fast against the bridge in a small whirlpool, while a mass of other debris flows past in the main stream. Lee eddies behind large obstructions are similar but in a vertical plane. They are a menace to aircraft and several unexplained accidents have been tentatively attributed to sudden pull downwards after crossing mountains.

In the case of the Ferrybridge tower collapses (p 110), a

contributory cause was thought to be eddying of wind around the towers, which were built fairly closely together in two rows of four. In urban streets, modern tower blocks can play quite unpleasant tricks with wind, especially when there are also funnelling effects. None of this can be exactly forecast or measured or pinpointed, but is a modification of weather of which one must be aware. Look at the photograph below showing a twenty-one storey building on an exposed roundabout

Distortion of wind round an obstructing building

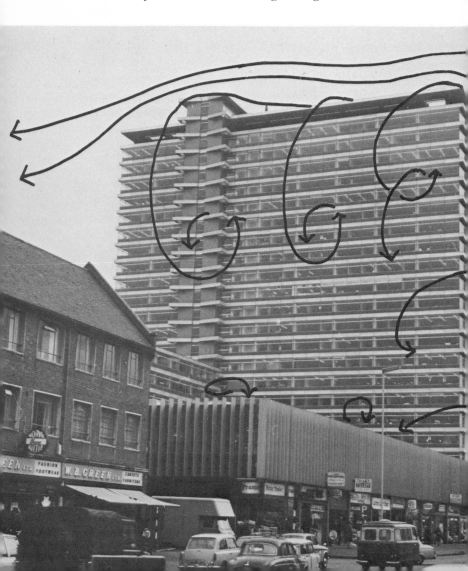

at Tolworth in Surrey. When it is calm elsewhere, it can be breezy around this building; a light wind elsewhere warns me that wind near Tolworth Tower may be fresh enough to wrench the car door out of my hand or smack the car boot up in my face when the catch is released. When wind is strong, it is safer to shop elsewhere. On one such occasion the fountain in the forecourt was blowing water about 30ft on to the road while the clouds were most obviously hurtling by in the opposite direction *towards* the building!

Because of the vagaries of surface wind, great care needs to be taken when observing true wind speed and direction. Wind socks on airfields are always situated well away from buildings and hangars; and where mechanical wind-speed indicators have to be installed in built-up areas they should be situated as high above surrounding heights as possible. Any yachtsman rigging his boat near buildings will do well to ignore his burgee till out in open water, gauging the proper wind more accurately by watching the clouds overhead. From inside a house, wind direction can be better noted by the smoke of a high chimney than by the smoke from a bonfire. Outside, too, this is probably a better indicator than the well-tried method of turning the head and feeling direction on the cheek.

PROTECTION FROM WIND

Understanding the behaviour of wind gives a lead on how to protect against it. Wind cannot be *stopped*, but it can be deflected into a more suitable direction, or filtered in order to break its force. If you visualise air as flowing in much the same way as you have noticed water flow you cannot go far wrong.

Harbour walls built out into the sea afford considerable protection to boats within, though this varies according to the wind direction. Probably the best respite is given when wind blows at an angle to the wall, though in slithering along its length it may pile up into a particularly nasty impact for a boat emerging from the entrance. When wind blows at right angles to the wall there can be quite vicious eddies on the lee side and perhaps some funnelling into the harbour entrance. The important thing to remember if inside a harbour is that wind is likely to be stronger outside than in. You may have valid reasons for thinking a forecast of gales is not going to materialise, but strength of wind inside a harbour should not be one of them.

As protection for the home, strategically placed walls or screens can work wonders by deflecting winds which blow either from the coldest or the prevailing directions. In open country closely planted clumps of trees protect the homesteads huddled within, by shredding the force of the gusts.

Within a garden, a pane of glass or board at the end of a line of cloches is an essential protection if wind blows *along* the line, else funnelling wind will whip away moisture and heat at a rapid rate. Otherwise, solid barriers are not considered the most suitable protection for exposed plants, which are relatively fragile and can as well be damaged by a strong lee eddy as by the full force of the wind. It is better to let the wind filter through a semi-permeable barrier of trees or hedges, though if moisture is in short supply open-weave or wattle-type fences can achieve the same effect (see also p 162). Research on the subject suggests that a 50 per cent ratio of air space to material gives satisfactory shelter, though even an open wire mesh is better than nothing. In theory, a barrier gives some protection for a distance equal to twenty times its height, and adequate protection to about ten times the height.

SEARCH FOR WIND

However, not everyone wants protection from wind. Yachtsmen most ardently desire wind, and the fact that inland sailors can find it along stretches of water which are maddeningly over-protected points to a certain discrepancy between theory and practice.

Opposite we see a stretch of the Thames at Surbiton. If we

consider it with the calculating eye of a sailor we can work out how the search for wind may be rewarded.

The far river bank has a continuous barrier of trees about 100ft high. If wind is blowing from the far side (gauged by sighting the passage of low clouds, observing smoke, or merely heard from a forecast) it will reach the river more true to strength in places where the trees are widely spaced and trunks bare than where trees are close together. Winter trees impede wind progress less than summer trees in full leaf.

Undergrowth beneath trees provides an even more effective filter than tree trunks, and in such places if wind is already light it will be only a whisper by the time it reaches the bank. By the time it reaches mid-stream it may have to fight against a counteracting lee eddy from air which has come over the top of the trees, and will probably disappear altogether. A canny helmsman may do best to hug the bank and catch what there is as near the source as possible. If such zephyrs are so slight that they only just keep the boat moving, even a clump of extra weed

Protected stretch of Thames where wind has to be sought after

growing out of the bank can put a final brake on movement.

The river bends to the right in the distance, and if this is the direction from which the wind is blowing, the trees will at some point cease to give protection. The decision on where exactly to leave the protected bank and strike across river to get the freer wind is crucial, and races have been won or lost on a few yards' misjudgement. Cloud direction gives a hint, also ruffling of the water surface.

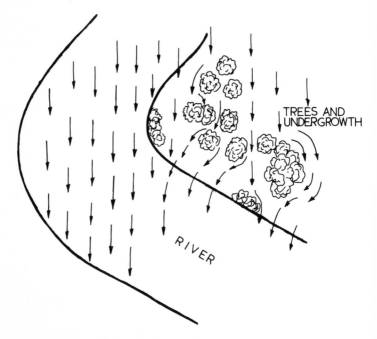

Trees and undergrowth break the force of the wind before it can reach the river

Look now at the nearside bank (p 115). An 8ft waterworks wall is surmounted by a further 6ft hedge of broom, planted for the laudable purpose of beautifying the scenery. The hedge is a classic wind filter and any light wind from the waterworks side gets dissipated by the time it struggles through.

But the calculating helmsman sees further ahead a hideous stretch of uncamouflaged wall, and his heart lightens. Wind puffs come over the top, eddy downwards, bounce back again off the wall and can be captured in a sail to keep the boat moving. Specially advantageous if the puff disperses before reaching a competing boat in midstream!

When wind is strong, the problem is to anticipate where the sudden bursts of strength are likely to capsize a boat. There is the bend in the river, where boats may suddenly be exposed to the full force of the wind; there is the passageway between sailsheds in the foreground which can funnel wind straight down to the river; there is the block of flats on the corner of the road, eight storeys high, from which this photograph was taken, where one can expect peculiar wind variations combined with funnelling down the road. This gets mentally docketed as a spot where 'anything can happen, fast'.

SEARCH FOR VERTICAL WINDS

On open sea, the quest for wind involves sizing up the chances of a sea breeze (p 25), and may well dictate a course close to shore in order to get maximum benefit, provided tide and navigation criteria allow it. In addition, a helmsman can utilise the known behaviour of vertical air movements under cumulus which are clearly visible in the unobstructed sky. The down-draughts from the rear edges of cumulus are from a direction more akin to that of the 2000ft wind than of the wind at the surface. They are therefore veered and stronger at a down gust, backing and diminishing again during a lull. Foreknowledge of this enables him to alter course to suit.

Over land, the sportsmen most interested in vertical winds are those who fly gliders. The tell-tale presence of cumulus will locate thermals if conditions are suitable for cloud formation, but otherwise terrain and surface substance may provide helpful clues. A dry sand or soil offers good thermal prospects in sunshine, even if the up-currents are shallow; a lake offers poor prospects. Lift over hills always gives air an additional boost upwards.

SEA-BREEZE FRONT

A tell-tale line of cumulus sometimes forms if a fresh sea breeze blows inland and at its extremity meets with a very light pressure wind blowing in the opposite direction. The sea breeze undercuts the warmer air from the land, which lifts and forms a line of cumulus known as a sea-breeze front. It is a temporary afternoon phenomenon, but serves as a sure sign of wind to a glider.

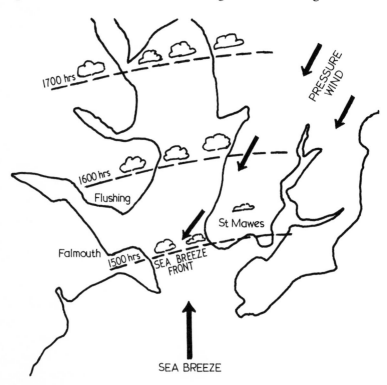

Sea-breeze front at Falmouth 13 September 1967

Such a sea-breeze front can affect sailing in coastal waters if the pressure wind is strong enough to put up a good fight against the sea breeze. In September 1967 I was sailing between Falmouth and St Mawes. There was a light NE pressure wind, but a light SE drift in the harbour estuary caused by the pull in of cool air between the heating land on either side. Off St Mawes was a glassy calm patch, topped with a few cumulus which had drifted off the land. By early afternoon, the southerly sea breeze was fighting the NE pressure wind successfully, had augmented the small cumulus considerably, and then proceeded to push the whole lot backwards towards the mainland, where the front died a natural death in the evening. The clouds looked dark and menacing so that a passing helmsman called out that a storm was approaching, but actually this was a typical deception caused by haze. The clouds were small and quite incapable of producing a storm, but they were as good as a marker beacon spelling out 'the wind changes here'. With an odd through-the-looking-glass effect, boats were approaching each other from either side of the sea-breeze front, and all running before the wind!

CHAPTER THIRTEEN

ISOBARIC PATTERNS

With an understanding of how clouds form and wind behaves, much prediction can be done simply by observing the sky overhead and the local wind direction, and working out the next stage in development. But the greater success which can be achieved by using the published isobaric chart each day is too satisfying to miss.

In particular, these charts indicate frontal systems which are approaching, but not yet showing any symptoms within the immediate horizon, and also the origins of air streams. Local wind direction can be very misleading in this matter. For instance, surface wind which blows from the south may have arrived at the end of a long haul across the Atlantic, in which case it will be moist; or it may have come round the south-east corner from Europe, in which case it will be dry. These two particular airstreams are so different in feel that a practised observer only has to put his face round the door to tell which it is, but other winds are not so easy. When the sun is shining, rising surface temperature can considerably camouflage characteristics of origin. A few hours of summer sunshine in a light northerly air stream, for instance, can easily fool one into thinking air is of much warmer origin than it really is.

Isobaric patterns are merely a shorthand method of conveying information about wind and pressure. They fall into a few basic types which recur endlessly in slightly different combinations but indicate roughly the same type of weathers.

Basic isobaric patterns. Compare the presentation of depression and fronts in this diagram with the satellite photograph on p 13

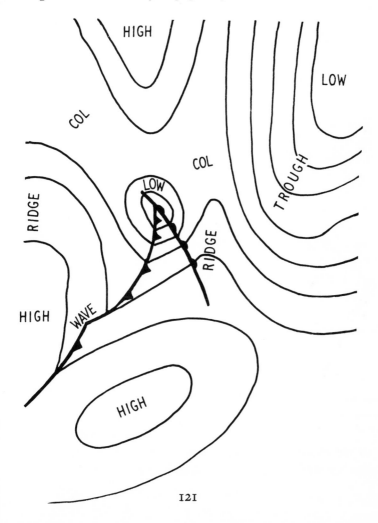

To forecast from them requires a step-by-step reasoning, a kind of mental addition and subtraction of all the factors we have discussed in the previous chapters. Maddeningly, it is not a quantitative arithmetic with exact answers, which is why I refrain from using anything as definite as a plus or minus sign in the examples that follow. However, as good a 'flair' for accurate forecasting comes with practice as comes to the skilful cook who knows her ingredients well enough to dispense with weighing.

PATTERN 1. WEST SIDE OF DEPRESSION, NORTHERN HEMISPHERE

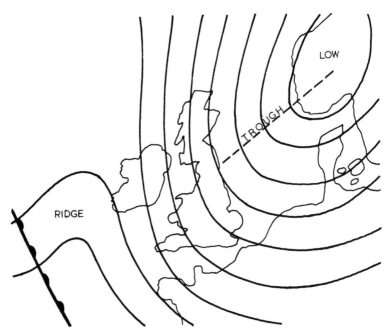

General

Wind blows anticlockwise round a centre of low pressure, therefore air stream in this pattern is of northerly origin.

By moving southwards, air warms in lower levels while remaining cold aloft. It therefore has a steep temperature gradient and is unstable.

It is an encouraging environment for thermal over the seas....TS and thermals over land....TL

A more stable situation exists in the ridge in the east because of divergence...DV

A basic weather of *cumulus* and *showers* is intensified or diminished by the following factors:

Towards intensification		*Towards diminution*	
Long sea track southwards and extra thermal lift..	TS	Radiation cooling over land at night.........	CL
Long land track and thermal lift..............	TL	Divergence at ridging isobars..............	Dv
Lift over high ground...	H	Interference of sunshine by spreading frontal cloud..............	F
Convergence near centre of depression and in troughs	Cv		

Application to British Isles

Northerly air reaches the British Isles via gradually warming sea and therefore already has a thermal impetus..... TS

To this must be added or subtracted the other factors according to locality.

By day:	Scotland, heavy showers.........	TL, Cv, H	
	Pennines, Wales, heavy showers...	TL, H	
	East coast, heavy showers.........	TS	
	West England, Ireland, few showers	TL ..... Dv	
By night:	Showers on Scottish coast and east coast	TS	
	Clear skies west and central England, Wales (leading to dew or frost, or fog if air damp).................	 CL	
	Clear skies, then spreading frontal cloud, SW England, Ireland......	F CL	

Troughs form rapidly during the day and affect any part of the country. They cannot be positioned till formed, and a published forecast may give only a general warning.

Special winter considerations

In the winter, over high ground and/or in higher latitudes, showers may be of snow instead of rain. In the British Isles, Scotland satisfies these conditions best and therefore has greatest risk of snow.

When the word 'snow' occurs in a forecast, beware how you visualise it. *Not* the robin on the Christmas card and the cheery snowball fights in the sunshine—that is *after* the snowfall. The reality of being *out* in a snowfall is blowing and drifting flakes combining with cloud right down to the ground over mountains to make visibility nil. It means hidden paths and lost sense of direction; numbing cold which slows and confuses the brain and saps strength.

To combat it successfully when caught out by accident is the triumph of a David against Goliath. To set out deliberately, knowing such conditions are expected, is to risk a tragedy from which there may be no returning. This happened to a party of schoolchildren in the Cairngorms in November 1971. Five children and a teacher died because of an unrealistic attitude to the power of the weather.

PATTERN 2. SOUTH SIDE OF A DEPRESSION, NORTHERN HEMISPHERE

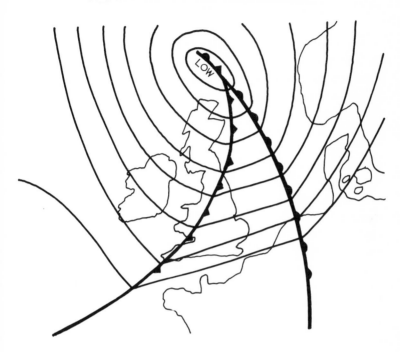

General

A warm front, cold front and occlusion are travelling on the south of a depression. Lines indicate *surface* positions of fronts.

Wind blows anticlockwise round a depression, in this case:

> SSW ahead of the warm front
> WSW behind the warm front
> NW behind the cold front

(Changes in direction of isobars really do indicate abrupt changes in wind and are not just artistic licence.)

Following winds impinge nearly at right angles to fronts, which therefore get full benefit of wind force and travel at nearly the same speed as the wind.

AHEAD OF WARM FRONT AND OCCLUSION	AT COLD FRONT AND OCCLUSION
Sheet cloud and rain or snow, perhaps 1-200 miles	Large cunimb and showers in narrow belt near surface front

Intensifying factors: Convergence near centre Cv

Lift over high ground .... H

Discouraging factors: Distance from centre .... d

Protection by windward ground .... p

Gradual mixing of airs .... m

IN WARM SECTOR

Warm air has travelled northwards and cooled in lower levels. Therefore it has a small temperature gradient and is stable.
Additional cooling will cause fog, or stratus if there is some wind. Appreciable thermal sources can overcome cooling and cause small cumulus.

Encouraging cumulus		*Encouraging fog or stratus*	
Thermals over land by day		Cooling over land, day	
winter..............	TL	and night in winter..	3CL
spring or autumn......	2TL	at night, spring, autumn	2CL
summer	3TL	at night, summer......	CL
Lift over high ground....	H	Lift over high ground..	H

Application to British Isles

The majority of depressions pass to the north of the British Isles and therefore bring south-of-depression weather to the country.

Both cold and warm airs come from the Atlantic and have smaller seasonal temperature fluctuations than do continental airs.

FRONTAL RAIN AND CLOUD
> Most in Scotland .... Cv, H
> Much in west England and Wales ..   H
> Least in SE England   .... d, p, m

WARM-SECTOR WEATHER

Southwesterly air reaches the British Isles via gradually cooling sea... CS
And receives additional cooling by lift over high ground on reaching the country .... H
Because of long sea track, air usually moist, and there is an inherent risk of fog or low stratus in coastal districts.

> Risk will be increased inland by cooling at night CL
> Risk will be decreased inland by thermals by day ...... TL

Winter: Everywhere, frequent stratus or fog, day and night .... 3CL.... TL

Spring (sea temperature at minimum):
> South and west coast, frequent stratus day and night .... CS, H
> Inland, frequent stratus or fog at night clearing by day with occasional cumulus .... 2CL 2TL

Summer: South and west coast, occasional fog or stratus, day or night........... CS, H
> Inland, cumulus by day, fine by night CL 3TL

Autumn (sea temperature at maximum):
> South and west coast, occasional fog or stratus day or night.............. CS, H
> Inland, some cumulus by day, occasional fog or stratus at night ...... 2CL 2TL

Special winter conditions

When a succession of depressions such as these affect the British Isles in winter, with intervening brief spells of ridge weather, no excessive temperature differences result between one day and another.

If, however, a ridge develops into an anticyclone of long duration so that very hard frost results, the subsequent sudden approach of a warm front can result in freezing rain or glazed frost. Rain from the wedge of warm air aloft falls still liquid to the surface, freezing on contact with any sub-freezing objects it covers. It is usually a temporary condition of a few hours until the surface front arrives, engulfing everything in warmer air. But while it lasts it is extremely inconvenient and dangerous. Layers of ice build up on twigs, branches and telephone wires, and convert all roads to skating-rinks. In January 1940 an approaching warm front gave freezing rain, and at the same time the high-pressure area obstinately refused to budge. For two days the rain continued to build up layers of ice, uprooting trees and telegraph poles, paralysing traffic and causing as effective a disruption of national life as the bombing raids that came later.

The actual arrival of surface warm air is likely to cause the additional complication of advection fog. By the time warm air is fully established, fog cleared and glazed frost melted, there may still be floods to cope with, for deep frozen ground takes a long time to thaw out and rain has no easy escape.

All in all, there is much to be said for living in Scotland or the north of England on these occasions! The chances are that encroaching warm air has a slightly lower temperature so that precipitation is already in the form of snow when it falls into the colder air below.

PATTERN 3. NORTH OF A DEPRESSION, NORTHERN HEMISPHERE

General

Part of an occluded front is being carried round the north side of a depression.

Pressure increases gradually via a well-marked ridge towards an anticyclone on the north.

Winds come from some easterly point.

All reasoning about the weather is similar to that for pattern 2.

WEATHER NEAR THE DEPRESSION

Frontal weather, intensified by convergence near the centre
and in any troughs Cv
diminished by distance from centre .... d
protection by windward
ground .... p
gradual mixing of airs .... m

WEATHER IN THE RIDGE

Generally stable because of divergence .... Dv
Small cumulus or stratocumulus if there is a
substantial thermal source .... TL or TS
Stratus or fog if there is a cooling agent .. CL or CS

Application to British Isles

Easterly winds come from Europe and weather reasoning must give added weight to seasonal temperature fluctuations of continental air. This can be intensely cold in winter, very hot in summer, but usually dry when leaving the continent.

Adjacent sea temperatures change much less according to season. The North Sea is a thermal source in winter (cold air over warmer sea)... TS
The North Sea is a cooling agent in summer (warm air over cold sea) .... CS
A long track down the North Sea appreciably increases the moisture of air in the lower levels .... M

NEAR THE DEPRESSION

Centres to the south of the British Isles are infrequent but tend to be slow moving and to outstay their welcome.

Summer: Continual rain, perhaps for 24-48 hours at a stretch, can cause severe flooding, especially if aggravated by drought-hard ground (floods in southern England 1968, p 102).

Winter: Cold air from the continent often produces prolonged snow, obstructing traffic over the whole country, south as well as north.

IN THE RIDGE

Summer: Air reaches British Isles over a cooling agent ....   CS
On east coast, night and day, frequent fog or stratus especially if after long track down North Sea ....   CS, M
Inland, fog or stratus clear by day, perhaps some small cumulus 3TL
Some stratus patches at night if air moist ....   CL M

Winter: Air reaches British Isles over a thermal source ....   TS
On east coast, night and day, much cumulus, small because of stability...   TS, M
Inland, over cold surface, fog or stratus night and day ....   2CL, or CL, M
In very cold spells inland, supercooled fog ....   4CL, M

In spring and autumn, cooling and thermal factors can more closely balance, and moisture content, related to length of track across North Sea, is often a determining factor.

Short sea track may give fine weather day and night.

Long sea track may give low cloud at night clearing by day.

Special winter conditions in Icelandic waters

Some of our main trawler fishing grounds are near Iceland. The prevailing wind in these areas is from the west and brings air at near or just above freezing level in winter. Sea temperatures benefit from the Gulf Stream and are several degrees above freezing, so that the sea is a thermal source.

Treacherous icing in trawler fishing-grounds off Iceland

Frequent depressions pass through the area, often with gales, and rapid changes in wind direction occur as the centres pass. When boats lie to the north of a centre, rapid change to north-east or east winds sometimes brings air temperatures down to the region of $-10°C$ in a very short time. The change in wind direction, apart from wind strength, raises a wild sea, the strong cold-over-warm thermal gradient between air and sea creams off the tops of waves as a curtain of spray, and the plunging of the ships throws up still more water. Sea water freezes at $-1.8°C$, and it builds up rapidly over the whole superstructure of any vessel that has acquired the low temperature of the air. The rapidity of the whole icing process is terrifying, perhaps as much as 40 tons in four hours over the whole boat (see opposite). There is little chance of escape. With strong winds blowing the boats must ride into the wind, which means further from shelter and nearer the ice-cap. The wind can change back quickly to a more normal westerly, but once loaded with ice, even turning a vessel is a hazardous manoeuvre.

Two trawlers were lost this way in 1955 and the whole nightmare came into focus again in 1968 when three trawlers were lost in one storm and icing was thought to be a contributory factor. The British Aircraft Corporation made extensive tests on the subject at their wind tunnel and research tanks at Weybridge, and as a result of their findings Imperial Chemical Industries have developed a synthetic wire, Parafil, which is a pliable tube containing hundreds of parallel laid strands of synthetic material. Parafil is extremely strong, the outer casing is very smooth and deters ice grip, and the whole wire is flexible. One smart blow at the base of a shroud and the ice which has formed along its length falls to deck where its weight can best be borne. The principle is extended to bulky equipment like radar by sheathing it in the same smooth synthetic, with air intake valves installed underneath. A slight inflation of the cover and the coating of ice falls away in large pieces.

The equipment has been tested in actual icing conditions and the results are impressive. But it will doubtless be a long time before all trawlers are adequately protected. In the meanwhile, when tempted to rile against the climate of the British Isles, spare a thought for those fishing in northern waters. 'Icing in coastal waters' is not a phrase they relish hearing in a forecast.

PATTERN 4. SECONDARY DEPRESSION, NORTHERN HEMISPHERE

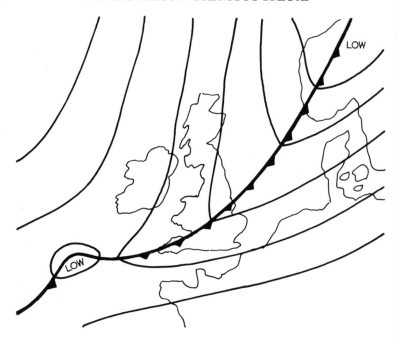

General

The south section of a cold front is trailing behind the north section.

Isobars impinge at widely spaced intervals, indicating slow progress.

There is extreme troughing of isobars and, like an elongated drop from a water tap, the bulging contour appears to want to break away from the main pattern.

A wave is likely to form on the front and may travel without deepening, or may deepen rapidly to an active secondary depression.

Watch for suspicious symptoms downwind, a re-gathering of angry clouds in place of the disintegrating frontal cloud, or a return of cloud and rain after the cold front clearance.

Be particularly alert if pressure is falling rapidly.

Wind changes should be predicted according to one's position relative to the new centre.

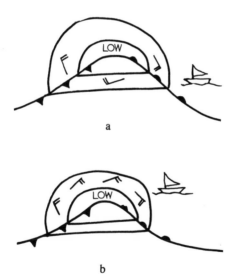

a

b

Cyclonic wind change; a) south of an approaching depression wind changes by veering; b) north of an approaching depression wind changes by backing

135

Applications to British Isles

Waves and secondary depressions can occur at any time of the year. They produce the types of weather that are indicated in patterns 1-3 but they often affect a much smaller locality.

Secondary depressions are most frequent in the south of the British Isles because so many Atlantic fronts are trailing by the time they reach there.

Funnelling of air through the relatively narrow confines of the English and French coasts frequently results in gale winds around secondaries which form in our south-west sea approaches and then travel up the English Channel.

Special summer application to the English Channel

Waves and secondary depressions have special importance to yachtsmen in summer, because this is when the majority are afloat. The English Channel is a favourite sailing water and, because of the high risk of accompanying gales, secondary depressions in this area deserve extremely wary attention.

In July 1969 an aged front trailed across the Atlantic, and forecasters were suspicious that something nasty was brewing. Light rain was falling over Cornwall and Devon by breakfast time, but nowhere was there any wind to speak of. Pressure started to fall in the west, by early afternoon rain was falling over the whole south coast, but even the Scillies only reported a modest breeze still. The first gale warnings were issued at 15.30, normal weekend boating activity was taking place in the Channel and an incredulous coastguard rang up the Met Office to ask if they really knew what they were talking about, since his weather was still flat calm. About the same time a small motor-boat with five experienced boating people aboard left Bosham for a last run of the day. There was light rain, a trace of wind, and a slight chop on the sea. They had no flares or lifejackets, and they were never seen again alive.

By 1800 hours gales were reported from Brest; by midnight a full gale was raging all along the south coast of England and north coast of France and many boats were in trouble.

This was a very sudden and violent deterioration, but it is misleading to call it 'freak' because it happens too often. Proficient sailors always consult a forecast or chart before setting to sea, and suspicion of a secondary depression coming up-Channel is often enough to keep them close to harbour. If at sea, it is imperative to study attentively every radio forecast to get latest details about the expected track of the centre of the depression. Earlier forecasts may only have been able to stipulate 'cyclonic wind', but the *direction* of change, veering or backing, may radically affect the evasive sailing tactics to be adopted.

PATTERN 5. ANTICYCLONE, NORTHERN HEMISPHERE

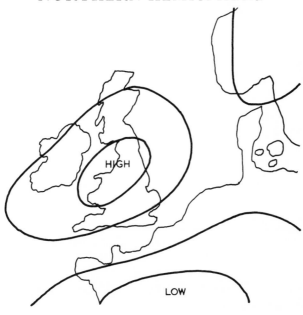

General

The centre of an anticyclone, more of a platform than a peak, is enclosed by widely spaced isobars. What little pressure wind there is blows clockwise round the centre and offers only slight opposition to the sea breezes which develop in the warmer months. The origin of the air mass is not obvious from one chart, but should be known from study of previous charts when the anticyclone was developing.

Sustained divergence gives extreme stability..............2Dv
Basic weather is *hazy with cloudless skies*, with deteriorations
    if air mass is moist .... M
    if cooling is excessive 3CL
    if heating is excessive................................4TL

DETERIORATIONS

Summer: High level thunderstorms in evening........ 4TL M
Winter: Frost, day and night .... 3CL or 4CL.... TL
          Fog, day and night .... 3CL, M ...... TL
          Supercooled fog, day and night 4CL, M ...... TL
Spring and autumn:
          Frost at night .... 2CL 2TL
          Fog at night .... 2CL, M 2TL

VARIATIONS DUE TO WIND STRENGTH

Increase in pressure gradient further from the centre gives stratus rather than fog.
Sea breezes decrease summer temperatures along the coast.

VARIATIONS DUE TO TOPOGRAPHY

Low-lying inland areas are the most prone to fog and frost.
High coastal ground is most prone to stratus when wind is off the sea.
Large inland areas are the most likely to generate enough heat to trigger off thunderstorms.

Application to the British Isles

Many anticyclones which affect the British Isles are breakaway centres from a persistent anticyclone centred in the Azores region, and therefore bring moist Atlantic air.

In summer: Heat waves are oppressively humid. Thunderstorms develop mainly in the Midlands and south England, and often drift across the Channel from France.

In winter: Weather rapidly deteriorates everywhere to fog or stratus.

Other British anticyclones are breakaway centres from high-pressure areas over Europe and bring *dry continental air.*

In summer: Heat waves are fairly dry and pleasant.

In winter: Hard frost sets in for long spells. Air temperature is higher on arrival in this country than on leaving the continent because passage over the North Sea has a warming influence. Additional radiation cooling at night, however, often gives temperatures far below freezing level inland and in low-lying areas. The west coast benefits from the warmth of the Atlantic and often escapes frost.

Weather cycles

The difference between winter anticyclonic weather in moist and in dry air masses is so marked that it can brand a country's type of weather. For many years the British Isles has had the reputation abroad of being a land of fog and pea-soupers, so that recent visitors have been very surprised at not finding themselves constantly embroiled in fog. The British in turn have been blasé about mild winters, rejecting as unnecessary luxury either double glazing or central heating. Recurring cold spells and catastrophes with burst outside water pipes have recently caused a change of mind—inside water pipes and central heating have become an essential feature of building specifications. Moreover, the traditional Christmas card scenes of skating parties and trade fair on the Thames have found recent echoes in our winter weather. In 1963 my family was able to walk across the frozen Thames at Surbiton, and on several occasions in the last 10 years ice has occurred on east coast shores.

It makes one wonder if the weather fashion is changing, and many attempts have been made to postulate long-term periodicities. There is a suggestion of a two-year cycle that seems to make even years warmer than odd years; a seven-year cycle linking sunshine and sunspot activity; a twelve-year interval between mild winters and an eighteen-year interval between cold winters. Nothing exact, of course, but discernible patterns that can be better substantiated than the folk-lore cycles such as forty days' rain after a wet St Swithun's Day.

At the moment scientists are looking hard at climatological statistics to see if there is a discernible swing back to the colder winters of the last century. In the first 40 years of this century moist westerly winds dominated the weather of the British Isles; anticyclones gave plenty of fog and depressions nearly always gave rain. Since 1940 the Siberian anticyclones have more frequently than before extended to these islands and with stubborn blocking tactics diverted the travelling Atlantic depression from their favourite path towards Iceland on to a more southerly track. Hard frost seems to be a more regular feature of high pressure than fog, and snow a less unusual feature of depressions.

CHAPTER FOURTEEN

DRAWING A WEATHER CHART

Once the habit of weather observation becomes ingrained and the value of an isobaric chart is appreciated, it is hard to do without one. Not everyone has a television set, or can turn on at the required moment to see the weather chart. Nor does every newspaper print one, nor every locality have ready access to newspapers. The extreme case is the man at sea, out of touch except by wireless but particularly vulnerable to the worse vagaries of the weather.

Fortunately, despite the immense organisation required to obtain all the information needed for a full chart, it is relatively easy for an amateur to draw his own adequate copy from very few clues. Five minutes of broadcast time can supply adequate information for an area the size of the British Isles and its coastal waters, though in complicated weather situations something like double the time is a more realistic allowance.

To facilitate reception of broadcast material for the British Isles, the Royal Meteorological Society issues pads of blank maps and forms, Metmaps, which are tailored to the shipping forecasts (see over). These also carry graduated scales for measuring wind strength from the distance between the isobars, and define symbols for plotting and taking down in shorthand style. It is an

GENERAL SYNOPSIS		at 0600 GMT July 6th		
System	Present position	(Movement)	Forecast position	at:-
L986	Stationary over N Sea			
W 1013	48N10W → E 30 kts → channel			
H 1030	53N 30W → 10 kt			

NOTES & ABBREVIATIONS

Systems: L = Low pressure) Insert central pressure
H = High pressure)
T = Trough

W = Warm front   C = Cold front   O = Occlusion

D = Drizzle   M = Mist   F = Fog   H = Hail
R = Rain   Z = Haze   Fp = Fog patches
S = Snow   T = Thunder
P = Showers   TP = Thundery showers   Q = Squall
(Alternative: Use the Plotting Symbols)

Use a vertical stroke to denote passage of time
e.g. D/ = Drizzle at first, or in past hour
R/P = Rain at first, showers later

s = slight   int = intermittent   c = continuous
mo = moderate   p = poor   loc = locally   cyc = cyclonic
h = heavy   g = good
occ = occasional   pp = perhaps   LV = Light variable

In CHANGE column of COASTAL REPORTS draw line
to denote pressure change. e.g. \ = falling quickly

BROADCASTING SCHEDULE

B.B.C. Radio 2   200 kc/s   (1500 m)
Sunday   Daily   Monday to Saturday
0303-0307
1155-1200   0640-0645   1355-1400   Clock
1757-1800   Time

COASTAL REPORTS at 0600 GMT

	Wind Dir.	Force	Weather	Visibility	Pressure
Wick	W'S	4			1008
Bell Rock	W	4		15	1011
Dowsing	W	2		5	1015
Galloper	NNE	5		5	1015
Royal Sovereign	NNE	2		5	1016
Portland Bill	N	3	•	13	1017
Scilly	NE	2	''	3	1016
Valentia	N'W	2	▽	16	1019
Ronaldsway	W'N	3		32	1015
Prestwick	SW'W	3	▽	13	1014
Tiree					

SEA AREA FORECAST

	Wind At first	Later	Weather	Visibility
VIKING				
FORTIES				
CROMARTY	W 5		▽	G
FORTH				
TYNE				
DOGGER				
FISHER				
GERMAN BIGHT				
HUMBER Smith's Knoll	W 4-5		▽ • cS	G
THAMES	NW 4-5		▽	G
	Var 3-4	NW 5-6	• ▽	M-G
DOVER				
WIGHT				
PORTLAND	SE 3-4	NW 5-6	• ▽	M-G
PLYMOUTH				
BISCAY	W 4-5	N 5-6	•	M-G
FINISTERRE				
SOLE	N 5-6		▽	G
LUNDY	Var 3-4	NW 5-6	• ▽	G
FASTNET				
IRISH SEA	W4	NW 5-6	▽	G
SHANNON	NW 5-6		▽	G
ROCKALL				
MALIN	NW 5-6,7		▽	G
HEBRIDES				
MINCHES				
BAILEY	W 4-5		▽	G
FAIR ISLE				
FAEROES	NW 4/5		▽	G
SE ICELAND	NW 3-4 / 5		▽	G

Mark gale areas   Connect areas grouped in forecast

Metmap drawn from the shipping bulletin broadcast at midday on Sunday 6 July 1969. (Metmap forms are published by the authority of the Royal Meteorological Society and can be obtained from the Society at Cromwell House, High Street, Bracknell, Berks)

142

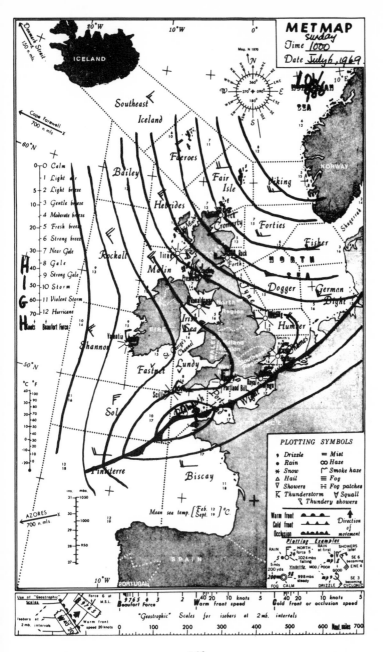

exercise well worth practising at home from the comfort of an armchair when nothing vital depends upon the results. You will be surprised how easy it is, and I have seen complete beginners produce very creditable charts after only one or two attempts.

The secret of taking down broadcast material is to do it quite automatically without trying to interpret on the way. Once you start thinking 'that is a gale warning for *my* area', you have lost the next fact, and if you try to remember what that was, you lose the next. Take down exactly as you hear, and if you miss one thing go on to the next.

SHIPPING BULLETINS

There are four main parts to the shipping bulletins broadcast by the BBC. Let us see, by studying p 142, how these are entered on a Metmap.

Gale warnings come first and these are marked with vertical lines in the extreme left-hand column alongside the names of sea areas. The areas are read in the sequence listed. On this particular occasion no gales were forecast.

A general summary comes next, very brief but often the hardest part to get down because it can contain words which have no official symbols. Those who know shorthand won't worry, those without it must develop a system of abbreviations readable to themselves; it is important to make a clear difference between 'Iceland' and 'Ireland', which crop up frequently and look so similar in a hasty scribble. Latitude and longitude positions of fronts and centres of pressure are no problem, because a mouthful of syllables translates into a few figures. For instance, '200 miles south-west of Ireland moving north-east' becomes simply: 200m SW IR→NE, but descriptions of locality such as '. . . is expected to lie along a line from Scandinavia to Humber to Channel Isles by dawn' are more difficult.

This general summary has a time date of four or five hours before the time of broadcast because it relates to the last complete large-scale picture.

Forecast wind and weather for sea areas for the next 24 hours follows. Occasionally one forecast will apply to several areas which can simply be bracketed together in the column to the right of their names. But in quickly changing weather situations each sea area may have its separate forecast and each expect a change within the 24-hour period covered. Absolute concentration is then needed, especially if the broadcaster is under pressure and trying to get extra material into a fixed time allowance. When overrun time is not allowed, vital material has to be left out at the end of the bulletin; this unfortunately sometimes occurs.

Coastal station reports conclude the bulletin, the observations having been made one to two hours previously. These are simple to take down and being the most recent information are the cornerstone of the whole chart and provide its time date. When plotting the weather, data given in the general summary and in the 24-hour forecast for sea areas has to be adapted to fit in with that time date.

When all the raw material has been recorded, then you can start thinking about what it means.

PLOTTING AND DRAWING

1.   Plot any centres of high or low pressure given in the general summary, also any fronts indicated, all moved onwards according to speeds indicated so that they agree with the time date of the chart.

2.   Plot surface winds and pressures for coastal stations. Wind shafts are drawn on the side of the station *from which* the wind is coming. Half a barb indicates one strength on the Beaufort scale (pp 35, 170), so that two whole and one half-barb, for instance, indicate force 5 or about 24mph. The barbs are always drawn on the clockwise side of the shaft.

3.   Draw in the isobars over the British Isles, at 2mb intervals, for even values. If the pressure readings reported are insufficient or of odd denomination, interpolate smoothly between those given.

Isobars will be evenly spaced if wind speeds are the same at all places in the area; they will be more closely spaced near stronger wind than near light wind. The direction of the isobars should be slightly veered from that given for the surface wind.

4. For the sea areas, we have to work backwards from the winds forecast for the areas. Select data from the early part of the 24-hour period. Plot the wind arrows in the centre of the appropriate areas unless specifically designated for one sector of the area only. Sketch in lightly the approximate direction of the isobars at that place (ie, veered a little from surface wind). Using the scale of wind force given at the bottom of the map for the *spacing* of the isobars, and starting from some factual isobar already drawn across the British Isles, build up the picture by deduction.

These brief instructions may not mean much till you actually listen to a bulletin, following the order with the Metmap on pp 142-3 in front of you. Next time, try taking down on a Metmap yourself and then plot and draw as described above. The method may seem hit-or-miss but whenever I have had occasion to make my own charts there has never been any vital difference between my effort, made at the time it was needed, and the retrospective chart published next day in the newspaper. When, quite by chance, I took down the shipping bulletin broadcast at midday, on 6 July 1969, before the disastrous storm mentioned on p 136, I was sitting comfortably at home. Had I been at sea and drawn the same chart, I would have disliked intensely what I saw and would have stayed close to shelter.

CHAPTER FIFTEEN

WEATHER INSTRUMENTS

Weather enthusiasts tend to divide into two broad categories: those who yawn at the very idea of having to read instruments, and those who gain a major satisfaction from regular recording of statistical data. The two groups often have a common interest in extremes of temperature or rainfall, which seem to hold great fascination for everyone. It seems to take the edge off the miseries of extreme weather if one can claim more misery than anyone else!

I would not in any way discourage enthusiastic amateurs from keeping climatological statistics, because they are of enormous help to research. But I would emphasise to those who do not share their interest that instruments are not essential for keeping a watching brief over the weather. One or two can be of great help, but much can be done by careful reading of the built-in instruments of the human body.

THERMOMETERS FOR THE PROFESSIONAL

To get true air temperatures, the meteorologist protects his thermometers in a Stevenson screen, which stands 4ft above the ground, has louvred sides to exclude direct sunlight while allowing reasonably free passage of air, and is not infrequently mistaken for a beehive!

Inside there are usually four thermometers:

1.   A mercury thermometer, in which the thread moves freely up and down the vertical tube as the mercury expands or contracts with changing air temperature.

2.   Another mercury thermometer, mounted horizontally, whose thread on expansion pushes ahead a metal index which remains at its highest position when the mercury recedes again on cooling. This records maximum day temperature, and the index has to be shaken down or re-set by magnet at the beginning of each new day.

3.   An alcohol thermometer, mounted horizontally, with an index contained within the liquid and dragged backwards by surface tension as the liquid contracts on cooling. When the liquid expands again, the index remains stationary in the tube while the liquid passes by, the index recording the lowest temperature. Re-setting is done by tilting the thermometer till the index drops back to the alcohol miniscus again.

4.   A mercury thermometer, identical to that recording air temperature and also mounted vertically, but with its bulb encased in muslin. The muslin is kept perpetually wet by means of a connecting wick dipped into a container of water, and the reading of the thermometer is called the wet bulb temperature.

Air which passes over the wet bulb described in 4 above evaporates water from the muslin according to its thirst. The drier the air the more water is evaporated. Fog, which is totally wet air, cannot absorb any further moisture from the muslin.

The actual process of evaporation uses up a small amount of heat, which is reflected by a fall in the reading of the thermometer. The greater the amount of evaporation, the further the reading of the wet bulb thermometer will be below that of the dry bulb thermometer and the drier the air. Dew point is approximately as far below the wet bulb temperature as the latter is below the dry bulb temperature. Both dew point and humidity can be evaluated from mathematical tables supplied with the instruments.

Evaporation cooling is at the root of the deep-felt conviction of many people that if one *must* do anything as foolish as bathe in British coastal waters, a wretched rainy day is less agony than a bright fine day. It is not so much the immersion as the coming out afterwards that is the trouble. On a wet day, little water is evaporated from the body during the short run up the beach back to shelter. On a dry day, enough is evaporated from the body to make one feel very cold.

THERMOMETERS AND HUMIDITY METERS FOR THE AMATEUR

Those who are interested in acquiring instruments for home or garden should be realistic about accuracy required: equipment should be reasonably truthful and quick responding to change in conditions, but does do not need the particular precision required by the professional. Quite cheap mercury thermometers, which have the scale marked on the mounting board instead of engraved into the glass tube, are adequate for everyday use. Apart from breakage there is little that can go wrong with them, and if there are errors in accuracy then these are a constant factor. The mercury thread sometimes get separated into small sections, but this can usually be remedied by shaking down.

A Mason's hygrometer (p 150) combines together, on a board with small top shield, a dry bulb and wet bulb thermometer. Ideally the container should be kept topped up with distilled water, and a satisfactory source of this is melted frost from the refrigerator, bottled after defrosting. A hygrometer is particularly important for anyone wanting to attempt frost forecasting by the method described on p 168.

A popular combined maximum and minimum thermometer is the U-shaped thermometer named after James Six, who designed it in 1872. The Six thermometer (also p 150) consists of

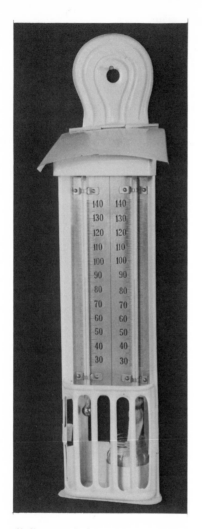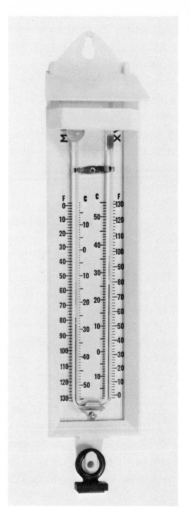

(left) Mason's hygrometer; (right) Six's thermometer

mercury in the bend of the tube, one sealed arm topped up with
spirit, the other arm also containing spirit but with a chamber at
the top to allow for expansion of the liquids. As temperature falls,

the liquids contract and the indicator in the sealed arm is pushed upwards; as temperatures rise, the liquids expand and the indicator in the open arm is pushed upwards. The final positions give the extreme readings on separate scales, and the instrument is reset by drawing the indicators down by magnet.

As an alternative to tube thermometers, temperature can be recorded by the expansion or contraction of a metal coil, and humidity by similar movements in strands of hair. These mechanisms are often mounted in quite small dials with pointers moving over a scale on the face. Humidity is usually expressed as a relative value—the amount of water vapour actually present in the air as a percentage of the amount which would saturate the air at that temperature.

For indoor use dial instruments are less clinical looking and some most attractively designed twin sets of thermometer and humidity meters can be bought. In the very cheapest ranges, however, there is probably less margin of error with the tube thermometers than with the dial type.

The important thing to remember about any thermometer or humidity meter is that they relate only to the surroundings in which they are placed. Readings taken indoors will tell you everything you want to know about living comfort indoors, but nothing at all about the weather outside. Fortunately, too, temperatures recorded outside need have no relation to those we manage to build up inside!

Instruments mounted outside must be shaded from direct sunlight if they are to record the temperature of air and not the temperature of the instrument as raised by direct radiation heat from the sun. A north-facing wall is best. Some protection against exposure from the full blast of strong wind is advisable, in case undue evaporation or loss of heat takes place for that reason alone.

For practical purposes, humidity is usually required in conjunction with temperature. For instance, a persistent relative humidity of 75 per cent could cause alarm about the spread of some particular plant fungus if air temperature were 20°C but have no significance in the same context if temperature were 5°C because the fungus would be dormant. At the lower temperature of 5°C a relative humidity of 75 per cent at dusk would be more likely to start one worrying about the risk of frost.

'BUILT-IN' BODY INSTRUMENTS

Every human being has his own built-in instruments. The body can detect warmth, cold and damp with enough accuracy to allow one to work out the origin of the air mass with little difficulty. I find a 'softness' to the warmth of a southwesterly wind, an 'exhilaration' to the cold of a northwesterly, and an unmistakeable 'cruel edge' to a winter northeasterly. If these adjectives mean nothing to you it is because they are my subjective impressions only. Each observer must calibrate his own impressions against the reported air stream of the day till he can tell instinctively the major quarter from which the wind comes. Every little clue helps, and as ailments do in fact react to temperature and humidity, the old music hall jokes about forecasting by the pain in one's toe can become a reality. If a corn throbs in a south-westerly wind, or neuritis pains shoot in the shoulder in an easterly, then those toes and shoulders become very individual weather instruments. Headaches are very frequent forerunners to thunderstorms.

Common to everyone, though calibrated with different degrees of sensitivity, are the thermostat mechanisms of the human body. We generate and radiate heat, and in order to deter the body temperature from rising above the normal level for health we sweat, making ourselves, in effect, wet bulb thermometers. If the air is dry, sweat evaporates quickly, the body remains comfortably dry, and we need to drink plentifully to maintain the sweating process. If the air is humid, sweat does not evaporate quickly enough to keep pace with production, and the body remains uncomfortably moist. The British, accustomed to damp heat waves in the 20°-30°C range which leave them drained of all energy, are constantly surprised at how pleasantly they can endure the dry continental heatwaves with far higher temperatures.

WIND CHILL

Wind speed considerably increases the rate of evaporation of sweat from the body and also the rate at which heat is whipped away. Any appreciable wind, such as a sea breeze, therefore helps one to adjust comfortably to a humid heatwave. It can also be a major factor in lowering body temperature *below* that which is comfortable or healthy.

The evolution of human beings has involved the loss of the major protection of fur. When a dog wishes to conserve heat it curls into a tight ball to raise the pile of its fur and increase the insulating air spaces round its body. In summer it will more likely stretch out full length to minimise the air spaces. Hair on a human being similarly stands on end with 'gooseflesh pimples' in the cold, but it no longer serves as anything more than a warning of chill. To protect our bodies, we must clothe them and we make the most of the insulating properties of air by using cellular material. An outer impervious 'windcheater' prevents wind blowing heat away from the air cells on the surface of the inner clothing.

When using the body as a thermometer to gauge the temperature of air, therefore, it is important to try and eliminate the wind chill factor which makes the body cold whatever the temperature of the air. For instance, it will be cold at the back of an open moving car after some distance has been travelled, but 'it' refers to the temperature of the passenger not the temperature of the air, which may be very hot. This is an essential forecasting maxim for anyone going to sea in an open boat. However hot the weather on shore, at sea it will feel cold. When travelling *into* the wind, normal wind strength plus the speed of the boat gives a combined extra volume of air passing over the body. When travelling in the same direction as the wind, the volume of air passing over the body is much smaller, the difference between wind speed and boat speed, and 'it' feels warmer. But if you travel one way with the wind, the return must be against. Never mind the feeling of suffocation as you struggle into pullovers and oilies, and ignore the incredulous stares of the sun-worshippers stretched out in bikinis. Your forecast will be right, and every bit of clothing will be welcome. Not only will the wind be cooling you but the surface of the sea will be doing nothing to help warm the air either.

Barograph

The best place to estimate air temperature is in a spot protected from the wind and direct rays of the sun. Outside the back door, perhaps, when taking in the milk in the morning, or at a widely flung window when rising. Changes in temperature during the night are often forcefully recognisable by the inadequacy or overweight of bedclothes. Try and relate such information to the weather you expect for the next morning.

BAROMETERS AND BAROGRAPHS

Though I do not urge people to buy thermometers or humidi-
meters unless they have a special need or interest, I strongly
recommend anyone interested in the weather to buy a barometer
(p 32). A barograph which records pressure on a rotating drum
is even better but is admittedly expensive (p 154). Pressure readings are most revealing about the course of the weather and
human senses are not able to detect small variations which may
yet be large enough to have forecasting significance. The actual
pressure value is less important than the direction and rate of
change, called tendency, and this can be shown by any reasonably
responsive instrument.

PRESSURE TENDENCY

The significance of tendency can be shown by considering the
weather patterns of chapter 13. Assume they are all advancing
towards the right of the pages, then the effect upon any observer
is the same as if he moves towards the left. Move a finger from
right to left across any pattern and note if the finger passes over
lower or higher value isobars. The results, illustrated by the
typical barograph trace shown on pp 156-7, show that
pressure *falls* as a depression advances (A)

> *steadies* as the depression centre reaches its closest position
> to the observer (B)
> *rises* as the depression moves away, with an abrupt rise
> at cold fronts, troughs and occlusions (C)
> *steadies* at the peak of a ridge (D)
> *falls* again as another depression advances (E)
> *rises* fairly rapidly in the ridge behind the depression (F)
> *continues to rise* slowly and persistently as a full anti-
> cyclone develops (G)

pressure *falls* if a depression deepens, even if stationary

> *falls very fast* if a depression deepens and advances

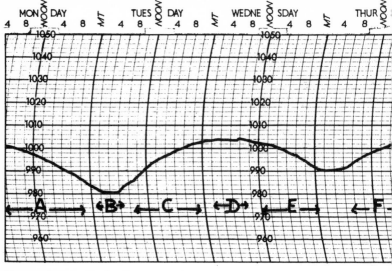

Barograph trace (for details see p 155)

  rises if a depression is filling and stationary

  rises very fast if a depression is filling and moving away

  may remain constant if a depression is filling but advancing

  Thus, falling pressure is generally a sign of deterioration of some kind in the weather, whatever the actual pressure level, with the possible exception of the decline of a winter anticyclone, when the advent of *anything* else may be welcomed as an improvement on fog.

  Rising pressure is generally a sign of some improvement in weather. Rapid rise, often behind an active depression, may indicate only slight and temporary improvement before another depression advances. Slow rise in the higher pressure range is needed for an anticyclone.

  Decisive changes in pressure are extremely helpful weather indicators, in just the same way that a child's crying is a helpful sign that something is wrong. The reverse, absolute silence in a child, or steady unwavering level of barometric pressure, tells

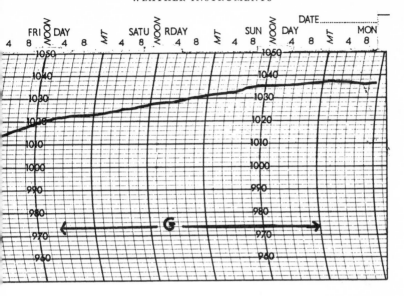

very little on its own. The present condition may continue, perhaps cunimb and showers; or the fine weather of an anticyclone may degenerate into fog; or a filling but advancing depression may bring cloud and frontal rain.

TENDENCY AND WIND

Wind is caused by a pressure difference between two points, and therefore it is not possible to read wind strength from one reading of pressure alone. However, winds are usually strongest near the centre of a deepening depression, so that rapidly falling or rising pressure, say one-and-a-half millibars an hour or more as a depression advances or retreats, often indicates that wind will increase, perhaps to gale force.

Once again it is a positive warning only, and wind can freshen considerably without any fall in pressure recorded on one's own barometer. This happens often on the fringe of a stubborn anticyclone, which refuses to give way to a deepening or advancing

157

depression. Pressure falls towards the depression, compression of isobars results, and wind increases in the ridge area without pressure fall or deterioration in weather.

MEASURING TENDENCY

To assist those with a barometer only, and no barograph, to measure tendency, instruments always have a second movable pointer set over the pressure-reading arm. This movable pointer should always be clearly different in colour or shape from the other. Whenever a reading of pressure is taken, the movable pointer is aligned directly above the pressure arm. The displacement between the two when the next reading is made will indicate the amount and direction of change.

Most small boats have barometer only, and on occasions when deteriorating conditions are suspected a man at sea may find it useful to take pressure readings at frequent and regular intervals and plot them on graph paper. It will give a disjointed trace, but can be specially helpful in indicating if a suspected wave is developing into full depression or dying a natural death.

All barometers have an adjustment screw by which the instrument can be set to record either actual local pressure or pressure corrected to mean sea level. The latter is best for comparison with published weather charts, and obviously is the same as local pressure for boats at sea. Instruments should be checked every so often to see that they are reasonably accurate. A telephone call to the nearest weather office or coastguard station will get the required value.

Barometers record accurate measurements of atmospheric pressure whether they are situated indoors or out. There is no advantage in fixing them outdoors, but every advantage in having them indoors. The most fascinating fluctuations in pressure occur precisely in those wild weather conditions when one least wants to go outside to investigate!

CHAPTER SIXTEEN

MANIPULATION OF CLIMATE

The basic purpose of forecasting is to beat the weather at its own game; to plan activities suitable for day or season and to protect against the more trying aspects of weather.

The question of how far man can actually *control* weather is wide open to the dreams of scientists. Producing rain clouds over the deserts and clearing fog at the touch of a button are not completely impossible but are not likely to happen tomorrow. In the meantime ingenuity can do much, specially when coupled with money.

INDOOR CLIMATE

Central heating and ventilation and cooling systems allow us to control indoor climate almost at will so that summer-weight clothing can be worn indoors all the year round. In a greenhouse quite modest equipment permits substantial lengthening or advancing of the garden growing season, while more lavish expenditure can create a climate greatly at variance with the one in which it is situated. Walk into the tropical plant house in Kew Gardens, London, and the thriving vegetation bears witness that it has been completely fooled into thinking that it is not in England but in its native latitude.

I understand that some ambitious architects visualise whole towns built under cover of plastic domes, thus dispensing with all the inconvenient aspects of natural weather. The prospect does not thrill me and I rather hope it proves too difficult to manage. What is not too difficult to achieve is some amelioration of outdoor climate by conscious consideration of site and by protecting house and garden within it.

CHOICE OF SITE

The climate of any area is that statistical absurdity, an average. It summarises temperature, rainfall and wind to give an impression which is recognised as valid; but in any one year or in any one spot within that area, weather factors may differ widely from the average. The lucky few choose their climate first and then select their home within it. The great majority, whose work dictates where they live, have climate thrust upon them but may still have some choice of actual home site. Many factors must be considered.

A south-facing aspect receives more sunlight and has higher

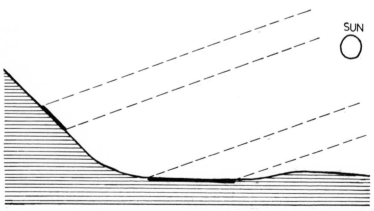

South-facing slope gets greater benefit from a low-angled sun than does level ground

temperatures than any other aspect. But a south *slope* receives even more warmth than level ground, because the sun's rays impinge more nearly at right angles and are therefore concentrated over a smaller area. The southward-sloping terrain of Jersey is invaluable for the early potato crop.

The benefit of a south aspect may be diminished if it is partly shaded by trees or buildings, but if these are protecting against persistent wind they may be worth some loss of sunshine. Sunshine may also be obscured downwind of large industrial smoke sources, which probably accounts for the fact that in Britain, with prevailing winds from the west, high-class residential areas are to the west rather than east of our cities. If a suitable south-facing slope also happens to be in the east of an industrial town, you have a problem of choice—but there is usually a problem wherever the site.

Suppose you avoid a hilltop because of wind exposure, and go to the bottom for shelter. You then become chief receiving agent for radiation cooling at night and suffer maximum risk of fog or frost. Even the wind problem is not necessarily solved in a valley if funnelling occurs down its length with certain wind directions. Compromise may be the best answer, halfway up the hill to get some protection from wind while being above the frost hollow below. But remember, even a slight dip in the ground halfway up a hill can be a frost trap if there is no outlet for the cooling air to drain still lower.

Dampness of locality is an all-important consideration for many in their choice of site, especially for reasons of health. Low-lying areas will accumulate fog quickest on days when the condition is general; highest ground has the least risk. But any marshy land, lakeside or river situation may do just as badly because it provides an extra source of water.

It is extremely hard to lay down any precise rules about choice of site because of the disproportionate influence of topographical features. A theoretical choice of site should always be confirmed by a discussion with someone who really knows the locality.

Whether climate selection has been possible or not, there are several things which can be done by way of protection to improve the small-scale climate, or microclimate, of home or garden.

PROTECTION AGAINST WIND

The best type of barrier against wind was discussed in chapter 12. The positioning of a wind barrier depends, of course, upon the evil to be remedied. Along open coastline, this is probably persistent battering which deforms and hinders plant growth, carries loads of unwelcome salt in the air, and penetrates every crevice in house walls and windows. Inland, the greatest need is probably protection against the coldest winds of winter.

Theory is mirrored by practice in the British Isles. Along the western seaboard, barriers are set to the west, and since there is no lack of rainfall, these are mainly high hedges and trees. They impede sunshine a little but the zone already has a high incidence of cloud cover, the crops that require a high ration of ripening sun having mainly given way to the more successful early market vegetables. In exceptionally exposed areas, like the western isles of Scotland with a high frequency of gales, fences may have to protect the hedges that protect vegetation before successful cultivation can take place. In seaside holiday resorts, miraculous displays of summer flowers adorn pleasure gardens within a few yards of the sea by the expedient of enclosing by hedge (see also p 163). The effective protection of a shallow hedge is sometimes increased by sinking the garden below promenade level, since frost is not usually a problem of a coastal summer. On a sunny day the temperature difference between these sunken gardens and exposed shore can be very marked.

Along British eastern shores, off-sea wind coincides with the direction of the coldest winds in winter. Since barriers to the north or east impede sunshine least, they are the obvious choice.

In towns inland, the major force of wind is already broken up by the complexity of streets and homes. It is the violent gusts and

High hedge, house walls and background trees contribute to a flourishing garden near the coast, but give a possible risk of stagnating air in still weather

funnelling which have to be deflected by strategically placed wattle screens or hedges. Other things being equal, a barrier to north or east against winter cold is probably best, especially since in built-up areas there are enough obstacles to sunshine without creating more. However, what is a north barrier to one person is a south barrier to another, and diplomacy is required if adjustment of microclimate is not to end in warfare with neighbours.

THE LIGHT OF DAY

Quite apart from the heat imparted by the sun, light itself is vital for the psychological comfort of human beings and for the healthy growth of plants. With miraculous ingenuity plants convert sunlight into the sugars necessary for their development. When

Distorted growth of a small tree shaded from light by a larger tree

deprived of adequate light plants become pale and spindly and make more upward growth than healthy specimens. Since the hormones which stimulate growth are activated by darkness, subjects which are deprived of all light (rhubarb under a forcing pot, for instance) will grow straight upwards; but a small tree shaded from light by a larger one, as in the plate above, grows faster on the shaded side than on the other and therefore leans towards the light. This should be considered when planting trees or hedges as wind protection. Fair shares of light for all.

Plants have varying light requirements. Some like short days and long nights and flower in spring and autumn. Others prefer extra light and flower in the long days of summer. Manipulation of greenhouse climate must also take account of this light factor as well as that of warmth and moisture. Blinds can decrease light to suit short-day plants, and electric light prolong it for those that like a long day.

WARMTH

Given a particular ration of sunshine for house or garden, heat traps can help to preserve it and improve climate. Cloches, greenhouses and sun lounges trap heat by day, delay loss at night and generally prevent dispersal by wind. For maximum effect glass must be kept clean, otherwise heat and light passing through are substantially diminished. This, of course, may be a requirement in very hot weather, when the climate can be toned down by blinds or an opaque wash over glass. In the rapidly altering weather of a spring anticyclone careful attention should be paid to the needs of young plants under glass. Fog or frost at night will mean closed greenhouses and cold frames, but by mid-morning fog may clear to another sunny day and temperatures under glass will rise rapidly, causing plants underneath to gasp for ventilation by afternoon. If automatic controls on windows are not available, vigilance must be exercised.

A south-facing brick wall serves admirably as storage heater, particularly in Britain for fruits which naturally do better in more southerly latitudes. Such a wall may benefit from a hedge or tree barrier behind it to break the force of strong winds and lee eddies, and give protection from the colder winter winds at critical spring bud-time. At night under a clear sky, a brick wall will surrender its heat like any other unprotected object, though plants will still glean some protection from its height. If in addition the wall is a house wall, then heat loss from outside may be partly compensated for by conduction of heat from inside the house. This is particularly true of a chimney-breast wall which is a good site for something like a camellia whose first buds are at risk in early frosts. With the added protection of a polythene cage during the coldest months to trap this leak of warmth from the house, spectacular spring flowering can be regularly achieved. Such a small amount of warmth, however, is not enough to protect really tender plants.

One disadvantage of a brick wall or close hedge must be watched for. If it runs along the lowest level of a plot it can impede the free exit of sinking cold air on still nights and cause a frost trap. A gap in the hedge or open-barred gate in the wall might help, or a hedge of low bushes with bare stems would allow cold air to drain underneath.

RAINFALL

Little can be done about the amount of rain falling into an area, but it is surprising how its incidence can vary in quite a small garden. A wall gives protection for a distance depending on the height of the wall and the angle at which the wind is driving the rain. In Great Britain the wettest walls are those with a south-westerly aspect, the driest those with a north aspect, but even a slight variation in orientation makes a difference. I have consistently grown successful tomatoes on a south-east wall, whatever the summer season has been like. The wall gets adequate sunshine without excessive moisture in really wet spells. I do, however, have the faintly ridiculous chore of watering plants even after rainfall, because the ground is still dust dry.

Quite apart from aspect, curious accidents can give markedly different water benefits to adjacent plants in the same bed. I have two hydrangeas, about 15ft apart, on a dry north wall, and one always produces markedly better blooms than the other. It happens to be situated under the bath overflow pipe. Every time the family tests the water coming out of the mixer tap, a little spurts out of the overflow pipe on to the base of the plant. The other plant suffers because I have not the time to keep it watered!

Watering by hose is the obvious way to counter lack of rainfall generally, and in many countries it has to be a daily routine if gardens are to prosper at all. Long and slow, like frontal rain, must be the method used, to ensure that water reaches the roots where it is required instead of running off or evaporating. In times of drought it may be even worse to water too little than not to water at all. With canny knowledge, roots strike upwards to reach surface water, making their roots more vulnerable to drying by evaporation.

VENTILATION

Excessive pampering has its dangers too. Ventilation and a free flow of air are not only essential in winter to keep cooling air on the move to avoid frost, but necessary in the warmer months to prevent stagnation and rapid spread of disease.

The best chance of success in manipulating microclimate is by protection in moderation, with a realistic appraisal of what is possible and likely to achieve success. Consult with experts on plants which will do best in the particular microclimate of your garden, and waste no time putting tender plants on north walls or frost-shy specimens in frost-risk hollows.

There is great psychological benefit from a prolific garden, or a protected and warm house: they foster the happy illusion that we really can control the climate!

APPENDIX

FROST PREDICTOR

The following method of constructing a night-frost predictor has been devised by L. P. Smith of the Meteorological Office. It uses all the factors pertinent to radiation cooling in settled weather during the months March-May, but does not allow for radical change in weather system during the night. It proved quite successful during test periods at Mildenhall and Bristol, and can be tailored to the individual microclimate of a particular garden.

A wet and dry bulb thermometer is required, and, for the first spring season when collecting evidence for one's own garden, also a minimum thermometer in order to ascertain if frost actually occurred during the night.

Read the wet and dry bulb temperatures at 1800 GMT and evaluate the dew point temperature from tables, in degrees Fahrenheit (conversion table on p 170).

Adjust the dry bulb temperature T according to the factors which discourage frost, in the following manner:

add an imaginary 1°F for every mph of wind speed   W

       an imaginary 1°F for every 1/8th of cloud cover   C

deduct an imaginary 1°F for every day since rain has fallen up to

       a maximum of eight days   R

For the first season plot the weighted temperature $T+W+C-R$ against the dew point D, using a small circle as the plot. Next

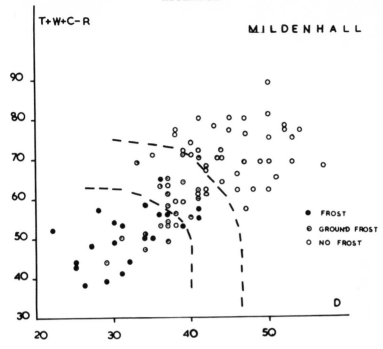

Frost plot diagram for Mildenhall

morning, read the night minimum temperature, then make a dot inside the last night's plot if there has been a ground frost, fill in completely if there has been an air frost, and leave blank if there has been none.

As the evidence accumulates, it will be found that two smooth curves can be drawn which roughly separate no-frost nights, ground-frost nights and air-frost nights. Once these curves are established *for the first season*, they can be used as forecasting devices thereafter. Establish the position of the evening reading T+W+C−R, plotted against D, and forecast frost according to which zone it falls into.

Reading of temperatures has been dealt with in chapter 15. Observing cloud cover should present no problem, but remember to scan the sky in all directions.

Wind speeds need a little practice, and the following time-honoured wind scale may help.

Beaufort Scale

Force	Speed (mph)	Description
0	Calm	Smoke rises vertically
1	1-3	Direction shown by smoke but not by wind vane
2	4-7	Wind felt on face, leaves rustle, ordinary vane moved by wind
3	8-12	Leaves and small twigs in constant motion
4	13-18	Dust and loose paper raised, small branches move
5	19-24	Small trees in leaf sway
6	25-31	Large branches in motion, umbrellas used with difficulty
7 and over		Gale winds over 31mph, difficult to walk against, and damaging to property and trees

Conversions to °C

Temperatures used in this frost-forecasting method are taken in degrees Fahrenheit, the scale still preferred by gardeners. The following conversion table is given for those whose thermometers record in Centigrade only.

°C	°F	°C	°F	°C	°F
7.5	45	3	37	—1.5	29
7	45	2.5	37	—2.0	28
6.5	44	2	36	—2.5	27
6	43	1.5	35	—3.0	27
5.5	42	1	34	—3.5	26
5	41	0.5	33	—4.0	25
4.5	40	0	32	—4.5	24
4	39	—0.5	31	—5.0	23
3.5	38	—1	30		

ACKNOWLEDGEMENTS

I wish to thank all those who have contributed to this book: Mr Theo Small of the research department at British Aircraft Corporation for the information about trawler icing, and 'Topic' Picture Service for the photograph; the Director-General of the Meteorological Office for permission to incorporate Mr L. P. Smith's frost forecasting method; Ambassador College, St Albans, for the photograph received at their satellite weather station; Mr Desoutter and Mr Shaw for providing photos which excellently filled gaps in my own collection; Henry Browne & Son Ltd and Casella, London, who supplied photographs of meteorological instruments. *Amateur Gardening* allowed me to use their drawing of frost cover for strawberries, and my publishers have performed wonders with my own amateurish diagrams by adding professional lettering. I am indebted also to my publishers for their helpful assistance and encouragement, without which I might have been tempted to give up.

INDEX